Eliot Attridge, Trevor Baker, Neil Dixon, Andre
Matthew Priestley and Bob Woodc

ESSENTIALS
OCR GCSE
Additional Science A

Contents

Contents

1. The diagram shows an animal cell.

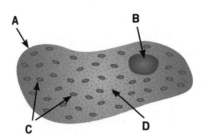

Which feature of the cell, **A**, **B**, **C** or **D**, contains DNA? [1]

2. All living cells produce enzymes. What type of substance is an enzyme made of? Put a ring around the correct answer. [1]

carbohydrate **cholesterol** **protein** **fat**

3. Chloe carried out an investigation to look at the effect of temperature on the action of amylase enzyme on starch. Amylase breaks down starch to sugar.

Iodine solution is blue-black if starch is present and red-brown if no starch is present.

Here is Chloe's results table:

Temperature of Starch and Amylase (°C)	Time Taken to Lose Blue-Black Colour (minutes)
20	24
30	11
40	6
60	37
80	Stayed blue-black all the time

(a) Explain the result for 80°C. [2]

(b) Chloe kept everything she used and did the same each time, except for changing the temperature. Explain why she did this. [1]

(c) Chloe decided to investigate the effect of temperature with a different enzyme (pepsin), which breaks down protein. Describe a suitable method for evaluating the effect of temperature on pepsin and explain why she would not be able to use starch to indicate enzyme action.

✏ *The quality of written communication will be assessed in your answer to this question.*   [6]

....

....

....

....

....

....

....

4. All living things respire. Explain the roles of cytoplasm and mitochondria in this process and explain how the energy released in this process may be used by the cells of the organism.

✏ *The quality of written communication will be assessed in your answer to this question.*   [6]

....

....

....

....

....

....

5. Plants use photosynthesis to produce glucose.

(a) Complete the word equation for this process.   [2]

.... + Water ⟶ Glucose + ...

(b) Sunlight provides the energy for this reaction.

What is the name of the green pigment that absorbs this energy?   [1]

....

(c) If a plant is grown in poor light, how will its growth be affected?   [1]

....

6. Damien wanted to investigate the number of buttercups in a field near his house. The edge of the field is lined with trees. Damien took three transects, starting by the field edge, walking away from the trees towards the middle of the field. Every two metres he placed his 1m² quadrat on the ground and counted the number of buttercups in each one.

He plotted the average number of buttercups in each quadrat in his three transects on a graph.

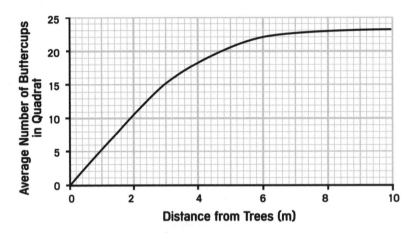

(a) On average, how many buttercups did Damien find four metres from the trees? [1]

_____

(b) Describe the pattern shown by the graph. [2]

_____

_____

(c) Why did Damien use the mean of three transects? [1]

_____

7. Petra thought that light would affect the growth of a seedling. She took four identical, well-watered seedlings in pots and placed one seedling (A) in a warm cupboard. She placed another seedling (B) in a refrigerated cupboard (by accident). She placed seedling C on a warm, sunny windowsill for most of the day and seedling D on a windowsill that was in shade most of the day.

After a week she found the following:

- Seedling A had grown tall, but was very thin and yellow.

- Seedling B showed no change at all.

- Seedling C was taller and looking very healthy.

- Seedling D was healthy-looking but had only grown a little bit.

Petra concluded that it was not light which affected the growth of the seedlings, but that it was the temperature which caused the effects. Evaluate Petra's conclusion, considering her evidence. Give reasons to explain your answer.

✎ *The quality of written communication will be assessed in your answer to this question.* [6]

_____

_____

_____

_____

_____

_____

_____

_____

8. Energy for cell processes is released by respiration.

(a) Most animal cells respire aerobically. What is the word equation for aerobic respiration? [2]

_____

(b) Muscle cells in the arms and legs are able to respire anaerobically. Give **two** ways in which anaerobic respiration here differs from aerobic respiration. [2]

1. _____

2. _____

(c) Energy from respiration is used for many processes in cells.

(i) What is the name of the type of protein that uses energy from respiration in plant cells to synthesise starch and cellulose? [1]

_____

(ii) What is the name of the chemicals made from glucose and nitrates using energy from respiration in plant, animal and microbial cells? [1]

_____

9. The diagram shows a plant cell.

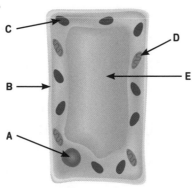

Not to scale

(a) Write the correct letter, **A, B, C, D** or **E**, in each box.

(i) Allows only certain substances to enter or leave the cell ⬭ [1]

(ii) Contains the genetic code for enzymes used in photosynthesis ⬭ [1]

(iii) Used by the cell to store waste materials and to regulate water levels ⬭ [1]

(b) Bacterial cells have different structures from animal cells. Give **two** ways in which they differ. [2]

1. ....

2. ....

10. Susie made some jellies for a party. She put some fresh pineapple in them but did not have quite enough, so for some of the jellies she used tinned pineapple. She noticed that the jellies with the tinned pineapple set a long while before the jellies with the fresh pineapple.

She carried out the following investigation to find out what happened.

In a test tube, labelled A, she put a 5g cube of jelly and added 15cm^3 of water.

In a second test tube, labelled B, she put a 5g cube of jelly and added 15cm^3 of fresh pineapple juice.

In a third test tube, labelled C, she put a 5g cube of jelly and added 15cm^3 of boiled and cooled pineapple juice (to represent the cooking during the tinning process).

Her results are given in the table.

Test Tube	A	B	C
Result	No change after 2 hours	Jelly disappeared after 1 hour	No change after 2 hours

(a) What conclusion could Susie suggest from this result? [1]

....

....

(b) What was the purpose of tube A? [1]

....

(c) Jelly is made of a protein called gelatine.

(i) What name is given to substances that digest proteins? [1]

....

(ii) What did boiling the pineapple juice used in tube C do to this substance? [1]

....

(d) What would Susie's results have been like if she had used 5g of chopped up jelly instead of a 5g cube? Give a reason for your answer. [2]

11. Biogas is a fuel made from the waste products of living things. It is made by allowing bacteria to ferment waste material such as cattle dung, human faeces and vegetable waste.

(a) Suggest why 'biogas' is given this name. [1]

(b) The biogas generator is airtight. Why is this important for it to work efficiently? [1]

(c) Generators produce two gases. One is carbon dioxide. What is the other? [1]

(d) Suggest **two** environmental advantages of burning biogas. [2]

1.

2.

12. Yeast can respire with or without oxygen.

(a) In bread making, yeast is used to make the dough rise and give the bread a fluffy texture. What is the name of the gas produced by yeast that does this? [1]

(b) In brewing, if air is allowed into the fermenter, alcohol is not produced by the respiration of yeast. Explain why. [2]

(c) In both baking and brewing, sugar needs to be present or added. Why is sugar necessary? [1]

13. A group of friends is discussing photosynthesis after a lesson.

Emily
Photosynthesis needs light energy from the Sun.

Jack
Photosynthesis needs heat energy from the Sun.

Darren
Chlorophyll absorbs the energy from the Sun.

Paul
The sugar made is stored as protein in the roots.

Grace
Photosynthesis needs oxygen to make the sugar.

Which **two** people are making correct statements?   [2]

_____ and _____

14. The diagram shows a variegated leaf. When exposed to light in normal growing conditions, the outer margin of the leaf is white and the inner part of the leaf is green.

(a) Students wanted to find out if both the green and the white areas of the leaf produced starch. Before the plant from which this leaf was taken was used in the experiment, it was watered and placed in the dark for 48 hours. Explain why this was done. [2]

....

....

(b) The plant was then placed in a light position for 48 hours. The leaf shown was removed from the plant and tested for starch. Where would you expect starch to be present? Give a reason for your answer. [2]

....

....

....

15. In the past, gardeners used to burn wood inside a greenhouse to encourage their plants to grow faster. Explain why burning wood could cause plants to grow faster, but could also potentially slow plant growth. Use information from the graph in your answer, along with your own knowledge of how light can be a limiting factor.

Effect of Carbon Dioxide Concentration and Temperature on the Rate of Photosynthesis

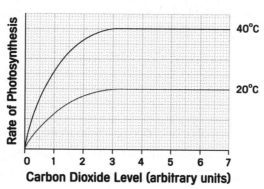

The quality of written communication will be assessed in your answer to this question. [6]

....

....

....

....

....

....

[Total: .... / 69]

16. Plants use photosynthesis to produce glucose.

Complete the balanced symbol equation for this process. [2]

$$\text{_____} + 6H_2O \longrightarrow C_6H_{12}O_6 + \text{_____}$$

17. Aamad carried out an investigation to look at the effect of pH on the action of the enzyme pepsin on egg white, a protein, which looks cloudy in a test tube. Pepsin breaks down protein.

Aamad's results are shown in the table.

pH of Egg White and Pepsin	Time Taken to Clear (minutes)
1	4
4	11
7	39
9	Stayed cloudy
11	Stayed cloudy

(a) The optimum pH for pepsin is pH 1. Aamad says his results support that statement. Do you agree? Explain your answer. [1]

_____

_____

(b) Aamad expected this pattern of results due to his knowledge of the lock-and-key hypothesis. Explain the lock-and-key hypothesis and describe how denaturing affects enzymes for both temperature and pH. Suggest why the optimum pH for pepsin in humans is pH 1.

✏ *The quality of written communication will be assessed in your answer to this question.* [6]

_____

_____

_____

_____

_____

_____

_____

18. The diagram shows a root hair cell.

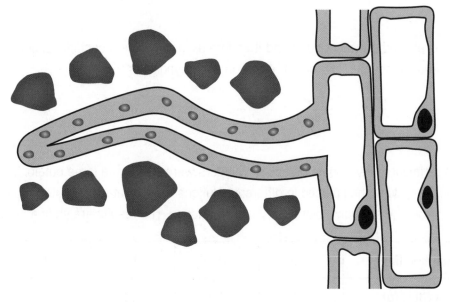

(a) What is the name of the process by which soil water moves into the root hair cell? [1]

....

(b) What is the name of the process by which mineral salts, such as nitrates, are absorbed into the root hair cell? [1]

....

(c) There are a large number of mitochondria in this cell. Why are these necessary for the absorption of nitrates? [1]

....

....

19. Which of the following statements best explains the term **osmosis**? Put a tick (✓) in the box next to the best answer. [1]

The movement of a substance against a concentration gradient

The movement of solutes from low to high concentration

The movement of water from a concentrated solution to a less concentrated solution

The movement of water from a dilute solution to a more concentrated solution

20. **(a)** Write a balanced symbol equation for aerobic respiration. [3]

(b) Rice is planted in waterlogged and therefore oxygen-deficient conditions, but its roots can still produce energy. How can it respire in such conditions? [1]

21. In an experiment to investigate osmosis, cylinders were cut from a large potato, blotted dry and weighed. They were then placed in different solutions of salt water. After 30 minutes they were removed from the solutions, blotted dry and reweighed. The results are shown in the table.

Salt Solution (M)	0.0	0.2	0.4	0.6	0.8
Mass at Start (g)	1.2	1.2	1.2	1.2	1.2
Mass at End (g)	1.4	1.2	1.1	1.0	0.8

(a) Why did the potato in the 0.0M solution gain mass? [2]

(b) Why did the potato in the 0.8M solution lose mass? [2]

[Total: .... / 21]

1. Draw straight lines to join the words to their correct descriptions. [3]

Word   **Description**

| Egg |

| Fertilisation |

| Sperm |

| The fusion of a male gamete with a female gamete |

| The division of the fertilised nucleus |

| A male gamete |

| A female gamete |

2. **(a)** What is the name of the process by which the cells in a zygote divide? [1]

(b) Why is it important that gametes only have half the number of chromosomes as the parent cell? [1]

3. Stem cells can be used to produce any type of specialised cell required.

(a) What is the difference between embryonic stem cells and adult stem cells? [2]

(b) What is the best stage of development to take embryonic stem cells? Put a ring around the correct answer. [1]

8 cell stage   **16 cell stage**   **32 cell stage**   **64 cell stage**

(c) Why can't cells that come from an embryo at any stage be used as embryonic stem cells? [1]

4. A salivary gland cell has the same genes as all other cells in the body. Which of the following genes would you expect to be active in the salivary gland? Put ticks (✓) in the boxes next to the **two** correct answers. [2]

Eye colour ⬜   Salivary amylase production ⬜

ADH production ⬜   Membrane protein formation ⬜

5. **(a)** How can stem cells be used to help in medicine? [1]

_____

(b) People suffering from diseases such as leukaemia often have chemotherapy, which damages bone marrow. Bone marrow transplants replace the patients' bone marrow, enabling new blood cells to be made. What must be in the bone marrow for new cells to be created? [1]

_____

6. **(a)** What is the name of the process by which plant cells in the growing shoot tip divide? Put a ring around the correct answer. [1]

| meiosis | fertilisation | mitosis | cloning |

(b) Give **two** differences between growth in plants and growth in animals. [2]

1. _____

_____

2. _____

_____

7. Marie carried out an investigation into the effect of light on maize shoots. She set up four plants, **A**, **B**, **C** and **D**, which are described below.

A	Shoot tip cut off and covered; given all-round sunlight
B	Shoot given sunlight from the left.
C	Shoot given sunlight from the right.
D	Shoot given all-round sunlight.

After three days, Marie's results were as follows:

A	Did not grow.
B	Grew and bent to the left.
C	Grew and bent to the right.
D	Grew straight up.

(a) Marie realised that the maize was responding to the light. Explain why the response of maize would increase its chance of survival. [2]

_____

_____

(b) Which maize shoot was the control in the experiment? [1]

(c) What was the **independent** variable in this experiment? [1]

8. Some of the stages of the human life cycle are shown in this diagram.

(a) At which stage, **A**, **B**, **C** or **D**, does meiosis occur? [1]

(b) Human body cells have a chromosome number of 46. If one of these cells divides by meiosis, what is the chromosome number in each of the cells produced? Put a ring around the correct answer.

                    23   46   69   92   [1]

9. Describe the main processes involved in the cell cycle from a single adult cell to new genetically identical cells in an embryo. [3]

10. The genetic code is carried within the structure of DNA. Complete the following sentences about DNA. Use words from this list. [4]

base	gene	single	double	triple

carbohydrate   protein   fat

The DNA molecule has a _____ helix structure. The strands of the DNA have four

different kinds of _____. The order of these in a _____ is the

genetic code for the production of a _____.

11. Carrie was doing an experiment looking at the growth of microbes in a liquid broth. The broth contained all the nutrients needed for the microbes to grow and it went cloudy as the population of microbes increased. She incubated the tubes of broth at a range of temperatures for 48 hours and recorded her observations. Here is her table of results:

Temperature (°C)	Appearance after 48 hours
10	Clear
20	Slightly cloudy
30	Cloudy
40	Very cloudy
50	Slightly cloudy
60	Clear

Carrie had predicted that the higher the temperature, the more the microbe would grow.

(a) When Carrie set up the tubes, she made sure that each one was prepared in exactly the same way and that all conditions other than temperature were the same. Explain why this was necessary. [2]

_____

_____

(b) Carrie's observations did not quite match her prediction. What evidence is there to support her prediction? [1]

_____

_____

(c) Carrie concluded that microbes stopped growing at 50°C. Was she correct in that statement? Use the evidence in the table to support your answer. [1]

....

....

(d) Her friend, Raj, did the same experiment, but he shone a light through the broth and used a light sensor to obtain a reading of how much light passed through. Raj said he wanted to be more precise than Carrie. Do you agree that he was more precise? Give a reason for your answer. [1]

....

....

12. When plants grow, cells divide to make new ones in certain regions of the plant.

(a) What is the name of the process of cell division in these regions? [1]

....

(b) What name is given to these regions of the plant? [1]

....

(c) The new cells formed in these regions are unspecialised. What does **unspecialised** mean? [1]

....

....

(d) If a tip of a plant containing these regions is cut off, it can be used to clone the plant as a cutting. Why is this only possible using these regions? [2]

....

....

13. The diagrams show two plants. Plant A was grown in good light in a warm place and watered well. Plant B was grown in the dark in a warm place and watered well, but was laid on its side. When they were initially planted, both plants were identical.

A   B

Explain why plant B has grown the way it has.   [2]

....

....

....

14. When two gametes fuse together at fertilisation, they form a new cell which will divide and develop into a new organism.

(a) What is the name of the single cell formed at fertilisation?   [1]

....

(b) What type of cell division produces gametes?   [1]

....

(c) The cell formed at fertilisation then divides into two cells. What type of cell division is this?   [1]

....

(d) At first these new cells are unspecialised. What are these cells called?   [1]

....

15. The diagrams represent two types of cell division.

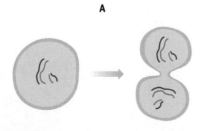
A

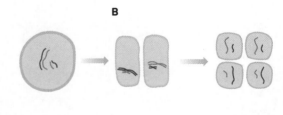
B

(a) Which type of cell division does diagram A represent? [1]

....

(b) Which type of cell division does diagram B represent? [1]

....

(c) Why is it important that the new cells produced in the process shown in diagram B are different from the parent cell? [1]

....

....

16. A group of students is discussing cell division.

Amanda
Before the cells can divide the chromosomes must be copied.

Oliver
Mitosis is the type of division that produces gametes.

Charlotte
Cells produced as a result of mitosis have half the number of chromosomes as the parent cell.

Kieran
Mitosis leads to the tripling of the chromosome number.

Miriam
Genetically identical cells are the result of division by mitosis.

Which **two** students are making correct statements? [2]

.... and ....

17. **(a) (i)** What is a tissue? [1]

(ii) Give one example of a tissue. [1]

(b) (i) What is an organ? [1]

(ii) Give one example of an organ. [1]

18. Parkinson's disease is a disease that is incurable and causes suffering. Treatments are being developed that use embryonic stem cells to repair the damage caused by the disease. Embryonic stem cells are controversial. Give the arguments for and against using embryonic stem cells for developing a treatment for a patient with Parkinson's disease and suggest alternatives that are being developed.

✐ *The quality of written communication will be assessed in your answer to this question.* [6]

19. Genes are part of a strand of DNA.

(a) Explain how a gene can cause a cell to make a protein. [3]

_____

_____

_____

_____

(b) Explain why a stomach cell will make the protein pepsin but a skin cell will not. [3]

_____

_____

_____

_____

[Total: .... / 66]

20. (a) The diagram below shows a plant shoot. The dots show the location of auxin.

(i) On the diagram below, draw how the shoot will look after five days of light shining from the direction shown. Add dots to the shoot to show the location of auxin. [2]

(ii) On the diagram below, draw how the shoot will look after five days of light shining from the direction shown. Add dots to the shoot to show the location of auxin. [2]

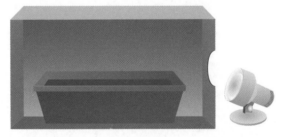

(b) The diagram below on the left-hand side shows a plant shoot with an opaque cap placed over the shoot tip. On the diagram on the right-hand side, draw how the shoot will look after five days of light shining from the direction shown. [2]

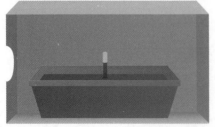

(c) Explain how phototropism increases a plant's chance of survival in natural conditions. [2]

21. In mammalian cloning, undertaken in a carefully controlled environment, a body cell can be induced to form a variety of different types of cell. Explain how this can happen. [2]

22. **(a)** DNA carries the genetic code. How is a single protein coded for in DNA? [1]

(b) The protein produced as a result of the DNA code is, most often, used by the cell to control a specific chemical reaction. What are the proteins that carry out this function called? [1]

23. **(a)** What should be applied to a cutting to encourage root formation? [1]

(b) How do auxins affect plant cells? [3]

(c) New plants grown from cuttings are **clones**. What does this mean? [1]

[Total: .... / 17]

1. Sticklebacks are a type of fish. A male stickleback will attack any other male entering its territory. Biologists discovered that the male sticklebacks reacted to the red colour on the belly of the invading male. Sticklebacks demonstrate this behaviour even when kept in large fish tanks. Researchers noted that sometimes the sticklebacks got agitated when a red Royal Mail delivery truck drove past and was reflected in the tank!

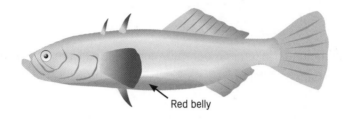

Red belly

(a) From the perspective of the home stickleback, the invading male with red on his belly is a change to its normal environment. What is the scientific term for this? Put a tick (✓) in the box next to the correct answer. [1]

Variable ⬡   Stimulus ⬡

Response ⬡   Reflex ⬡

(b) The stickleback was responding rapidly and involuntarily to the invading stickleback.

(i) What do we call this type of response? [1]

(ii) Why do simple organisms respond in this way to changes in their environments? [1]

(c) Why did the sticklebacks get agitated by the Royal Mail delivery truck driving past? [1]

(d) Fiesa decides to try to prove it is the red colour that the stickleback is reacting to. Describe an experiment that she could carry out which would prove whether or not it is the red colour that the territorial stickleback reacts to.

🖋 *The quality of written communication will be assessed in your answer to this question.* [6]

2. A maternity unit at a hospital has provided data about newborn babies and their success in some tests.

Weight	Percentage of Newborn Babies Passing Test		
	Step	Grasp	Startle
Normal	98%	99%	100%
25% lower than normal	89%	92%	94%
50% lower than normal	70%	71%	69%

(a) What is the hospital testing for? [1]

....

(b) What is the correlation behind the results? [1]

....

....

(c) Briefly describe what each test involves. [3]

Step: ....

Grasp: ....

Startle: ....

(d) If the number of babies born with 50% lower-than-normal birth weight was 340, how many **failed** the grasp test? Show your working. [2]

....

....

(e) State one reflex that adult humans possess. [1]

....

(f) What type of signal is sent along neurons in the nervous system? [1]

....

(g) Give **three** differences between nerve signals and hormones. [3]

....

....

....

3. Joss is cooking sweetcorn in the microwave. When he touches the cup, it is extremely hot and he drops the cup from his hand.

(a) The chart below shows a range of possible steps that took place which led to Joss carrying out this physical response. Draw straight lines between one box in each column to show the correct order of events. [2]

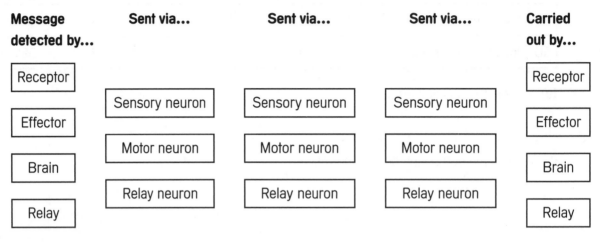

(b) What is this sequence called? [1]

_____

(c) Claire decides to carry out an experiment to see how fast people's reactions are. She times how long it takes a person to catch a £10 note dropped between two fingers. The results are shown below.

Test	1	2	3	4	5	6	7	8	9	10
Time Taken (s)	2.0	2.1	1.9	1.7	1.6	1.6	1.5	3.1	1.2	0.9

(i) What is the **range** of values in Claire's experiment? [1]

_____

(ii) Claire reports the mean as being 1.6s. Explain how she calculated this result. [2]

_____

_____

(d) Joss tells Claire that her data show a correlation. What is the correlation? [1]

_____

_____

4. Pavlov was a scientist who discovered what is now called **conditioned reflexes**. His experiments on dogs showed how this type of reflex took place.

(a) The four stages, **A**, **B**, **C** and **D**, describe the processes involved in developing a conditioned reflex. They are not in the correct order. Put the stages in the correct order by writing the letters in the empty boxes. [1]

A A bell is rung repeatedly whenever the dog is shown meat.

B Eventually the bell is rung without meat present.

C The dog is given the meat each time.

D The dog salivates as if meat were present.

Start | | | | |

(b) In 2003, scientists showed that when humans were shown abstract images together with smelling either peanuts or vanilla essence, they then associated the images with peanuts or vanilla. This is a form of conditioned reflex. Why should this finding not be a surprise? Put ticks (✓) in the boxes next to the **two best** answers. [1]

This is the same experiment that Pavlov undertook. ◯   Humans are intelligent. ◯

Humans are also animals. ◯   Scientists published this before. ◯

5. Read the newspaper article below.

> ## To Walk Again
>
> In 2011, a man who had been paralysed from the waist in a terrible car accident was able to walk again. The man had severed his spinal cord in the accident. Researchers at an American university gave the man daily electrical impulses which, after a period of time, enabled him to move his legs again. The man is now learning how to walk again and has a new lease of life.

(a) Why are patients paralysed if the spinal cord is severed? [1]

....

(b) The researchers are claiming a breakthrough in reversing paralysis. However, other scientists urge caution, warning that it should not be assumed that everyone will benefit from this in the future. Which of the following are the two **best** reasons behind the warning? Put ticks (✓) in the boxes next to the best answers. [1]

Electricity is not available everywhere, so people won't necessarily benefit. ◯

The sample size for this experiment is one. ◯

The work needs to first win the Nobel Prize. ◯

The mechanism behind the experiment is not understood. ◯

6. The table below shows the average speed that nerve impulses take travelling through neurons of different thicknesses.

Neuron Diameter (μm)	Speed of Nerve Impulse (m/s)
1	2
2	6
3	15
4	19
5	25
6	28

(a) Plot a **scatter graph** of the data on the grid below. [3]

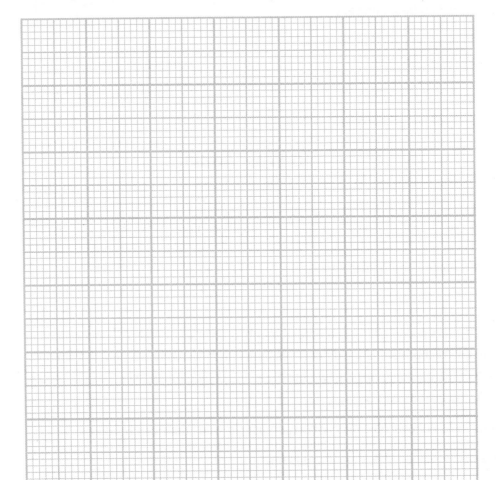

(b) What conclusion can be made from the graph? [1]

....

(c) What gives the neuron an increased diameter? Put a tick (✓) in the box next to the best answer. [1]

A protein-based coating ⬭ An insulation layer ⬭

A plastic coating ⬭ A fatty sheath ⬭

7. **(a)** Mammals have complex brains. Approximately how many neurons are in a mammalian brain? Put a ring around the correct answer. [1]

hundreds **thousands** **millions** **billions**

(b) What happens to the number of synapses as the brain grows in the first years of life? [1]

....

(c) (i) How do the pathways between neurons become stimulated? [1]

....

(ii) How do the pathways become strengthened? [1]

....

(iii) What happens to the pathways that are not used regularly? [1]

....

(d) Explain why you are able to learn some skills through repetition. [2]

....

....

....

....

8. **(a)** Explain how physiological techniques are used to map the regions of the cerebral cortex. [2]

....

....

....

(b) What technique was used to create this image? [1]

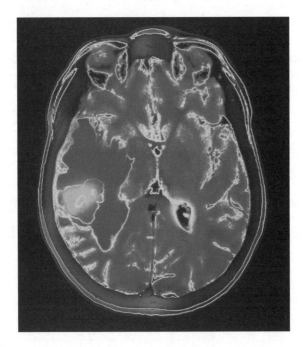

(c) Biologists at the Impaired Consciousness Research Group at the Wolfson Brain Imaging Centre are developing techniques to show whether people in comas retain any form of awareness. They do this by using an MRI scanner and asking the seemingly-unconscious patient questions about their life.

When carrying out the experiment the scientists ask questions, which only the patient and their family might know the answers to. The patient is asked to think about playing tennis for 'yes' and walking around the rooms of a house for 'no'. The doctors carrying out the study do not know the answers to the questions that the patient may or may not answer.

(i) Why did the scientists choose playing tennis and walking around the house as subjects for the patients to think about? Put a tick (✓) in the box next to the **best** answer. [1]

These were the scientists' favourite hobbies. ◯

The activities use different parts of the brain. ◯

The patients all play tennis. ◯

There is no difference between the activities in the brain. ◯

(ii) Why is it important that the scientists carrying out the experiment do not know the answers to the questions? [1]

....

....

9. An experiment was set up to investigate how we remember information. Participants were given a set of numbers and asked to memorise them for 30 seconds. Some of the groups also had loud music playing as they memorised the numbers. The treatments for the experiment are shown below.

Group 1 (Quiet)	12342234	32344234	52346234	72348234
Group 2 (Loud Music)	12342234	32344234	52346234	72348234
Group 3 (Quiet)	12342297	22971234	22349723	39218475
Group 4 (Loud Music)	12342297	22971234	22349723	39218475

(a) Suggest which would be the most successful group in this experiment. Give **two** reasons for your answer. [3]

(b) Write a suitable hypothesis for this experiment. [1]

(c) Other than time to memorise, state a variable that it would be important to control for this experiment. [1]

(d) If the experiment was repeated for the same groups but with different numbers, what, if anything, would happen over time to the success rate of the groups which had loud music playing? Explain your answer. [2]

(e) The experiment is repeated by other researchers, this time using an MRI scanner. What added information would this procedure tell us? [2]

[Total: _____ / 59]

10. Insulin is a hormone released from glands in the pancreas when its cells 'sense' blood glucose levels are high. Suggest why this response is more efficient than the brain transmitting nervous impulses to cause this to happen. [2]

_____

_____

_____

11. The tongue is a sense organ that can detect a variety of tastes from the particles present in food. Taste buds contain specialised cells with microvilli, which respond to the different tastes.

In 1901, a German scientist, H.P. Hanig, tried measuring the relative sensitivity of the tongue to the then four basic tastes. Based on the statements of his volunteers, he came to the conclusion that the four tastes varied over the tongue, as in the diagram below.

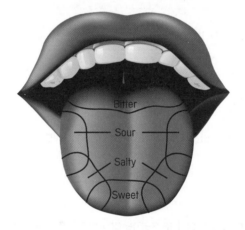

Hanig reported his findings in a graph but with no scale on the y-axis.

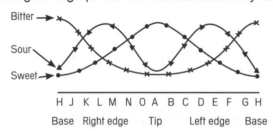

In 1974, Virginia Collings looked at the work again but concluded that the differences in taste receptors were negligible across the tongue. It is now accepted that each taste bud can detect a range of tastes (sweet, sour, salt, bitter and umami). There is no need to sub-divide the tongue into different areas.

(a) Use the information provided and your own knowledge to explain how the taste bud detects taste and how the signal is transmitted to the brain.

✎ The quality of written communication will be assessed in your answer to this question. [6]

....

....

....

....

....

....

....

....

....

(b) Although Collings disproved the original research in 1974, textbooks still continued to show the tongue-taste map into the 1980s.

Which of the following explain why the fallacy of the tongue-taste map persisted for so long? Put ticks (✓) in the boxes next to the **two** best answers. [2]

The original research had been published. ⬭

The tongue map idea was powerful and difficult to counter. ⬭

The modern research took place a long time after the original research. ⬭

People's tongues have changed over the years. ⬭

(c) Suggest **two** ways why having no scale on the *y*-axis of Hanig's graph was such a problem. [2]

....

....

....

12. A new drug, MIRI, has been produced that interferes with the neurotransmitter, serotonin. Biologists are trying to explain how the drug works by looking at how nerve impulses are affected in people taking the drug.

(a) The five stages, **A**, **B**, **C**, **D** and **E**, describe the normal process of nerve impulse transmission. They are not in the correct order. Put the stages in the correct order by writing the letters in the empty boxes. [2]

    A   The serotonin fits into receptors on the relay neuron.

    B   The serotonin is reabsorbed into the sensory neuron.

    C   The serotonin is produced by the sensory neuron.

    D   Once the receptors are all full, an impulse is initiated in the relay neuron.

    E   The serotonin enters the synapse.

Start					

(b) Users of the new drug report that they feel elated (happy).

    (i) Which current drug is most like MIRI? [1]

    (ii) Suggest why the drug increases the concentration of serotonin in the synapse. [1]

    (iii) Why would this cause the effects noted? [1]

(c) The Government announces that it will ban MIRI. A group of friends is discussing the proposed ban.

Holly
I want to know the long-term medical effects of taking MIRI.

Lucy
I want to know how long MIRI stays in the body.

Michael
I want to know whether taking MIRI is good or bad.

Samuel
I want to know how much MIRI can be safely taken.

Who is asking a question that science **cannot** answer? [1]

13. In 2007, it was reported that an 11-year-old girl, who suffered from an extremely rare and debilitating form of epilepsy, had undergone a hemispherectomy (an operation to remove half of her brain). The purpose was to remove the part of the brain that was causing the epilepsy.

Having had half of the brain removed, surgeons filled the cavity with sterile water so that the remaining half of the brain was supported. Surgeons do not fully understand how this operation works – it is amazing that the operation does not leave the patient senseless and immobile.

(a) What would be the basis for deciding whether or not to give a patient a hemispherectomy? Put a tick (✓) in the box next to the **best** answer. [1]

The prestige the surgeons get from carrying out the operation outweighs the risk of it.

The benefit to the patient outweighs the cost of the operation.

The benefit to the patient outweighs the risk of the operation.

The benefit to the parents of the patient outweighs the risk of the operation.

(b) The girl recovered the ability to speak and had no signs of the epilepsy following the operation. Suggest what happened in the brain to enable her to do this. [1]

[Total: .... / 20]

C4 | Chemical Patterns

1. Five students watch their teacher demonstrate the reactions of lithium, sodium and potassium with water. They talk about what they see.

Joe
The sodium floated on the surface of the water.

James
The alkali metals seem to be getting more reactive as you go down the group.

Zoe
Sodium and potassium melt during the reaction with water but lithium does not.

Caroline
A flammable gas is produced during the reaction of alkali metals with water. A different colour flame can be seen for each different metal.

Richard
I think that caesium will explode when it is dropped into water.

(a) Which student is making a prediction rather than an observation? [1]

(b) Which student has identified a trend using observations from the experiment? [1]

(c) What gas is Caroline talking about? [1]

....

(d) James says that he has seen the reaction of caesium with water on a television programme. Is this a reliable source of information about this reaction? Explain your answer. [1]

....

....

....

2. **(a)** Complete the following table. [4]

	Mass	Charge	Where in the Atom is it Found?
Proton			In the nucleus
Electron	Approx. 0	Negative	Orbiting the nucleus
Neutron	1		

(b) What is the overall electrical charge on an atom? Explain your answer. [2]

....

....

....

(c) Complete the statement below about how many electrons fit into each electron shell. [3]

Up to .... electrons fit into the first shell; up to .... fit

into the second shell; up to .... fit into the third shell.

(d) Work out the electron configurations of the following elements, writing them with numbers to show the number of electrons in each shell. For example, boron has two electrons in its first shell and three in its second shell so it is written 2.3.

(i) Carbon (6 electrons): .... [1]

(ii) Chlorine (17 electrons): .... [1]

(iii) Sodium (11 electrons): .... [1]

(iv) Potassium (19 electrons): .... [1]

(e) What is the link between the electron configuration of an element and its group number? [1]

(f) What is the link between the electron configuration of an element and its period number? [1]

(g) An atom has four electrons in its third shell. What element is it? [1]

3. **(a)** Complete this paragraph. [3]

When atoms of an element are given lots of energy, for example, by heating them, they give off light

of a particular _____. For example, sodium compounds always give off orange

light, as seen in many street lamps. This light can be analysed using a technique called

_____ which helps chemists to identify the elements in stars in outer space.

This technique can be used to produce a line _____ which is specific to that

element.

(b) Describe how to perform a flame test to distinguish between lithium chloride, sodium chloride and potassium chloride. You do not need to know the colours produced by these compounds.

🖉 *The quality of written communication will be assessed in your answer to this question.* [6]

4. **(a)** Draw straight lines to show the correct meaning of each of the hazard symbols. [3]

Hazard symbol   **Meaning**

Harmful

Flammable

Corrosive

Oxidising agent

(b) Describe a precaution you would take when working with a flammable chemical. [1]

....

(c) Describe two precautions you would take when working with a harmful chemical. [2]

....

....

5. **(a)** Write down the symbols of four elements in Group 1. [1]

....

(b) What name is given to elements in Group 1? [1]

....

(c) Why are the Group 1 elements stored under oil? [1]

....

(d) Use your understanding of trends in the periodic table to complete the following table. Make sensible estimates where necessary. [3]

Element	Melting Point (K)	Boiling Point (K)	Formula of Chloride
Lithium	453		LiCl
Sodium	370	1156	
Potassium		1032	KCl

(e) Describe what you would **see** when a piece of sodium is put into a large bowl of cold water. [2]

_____

_____

(f) (i) Write a word equation for the reaction between lithium and water. [2]

_____

(ii) Write a word equation for the reaction between sodium and chlorine. [2]

_____

(g) What happens to the reactivity of the Group 1 elements as you go down the group? [1]

_____

(h) Make a prediction about how caesium would react with water. [1]

_____

_____

(i) Estimate the melting point of rubidium, in Kelvin. [1]

_____ K

6. This question is about the Group 7 elements.

(a) What name is given to the elements in Group 7? Put a tick (✓) in the box next to the correct answer. [1]

The halogens ☐

The noble gases ☐

The transition metals ☐

The salts ☐

(b) The formula of chlorine is Cl_2. Which of the diagrams shows a chlorine molecule? Put a ring around the correct answer. [1]

A   B   C   D

(c) Complete the following table. Make sensible estimates where necessary. [4]

Element	Formula	Appearance at Room Temperature (colour and state)	Melting Point (K)	Boiling Point (K)
Chlorine	Cl_2			239
Bromine		Orange/brown liquid, evaporates easily	266	332
Iodine	I_2	Grey solid, sublimes to purple vapour	387	

(d) Alex heats a small piece of lithium metal and places it into a gas jar full of chlorine gas. A reaction occurs that releases heat and light energy. A single product is made, which is a white solid salt. Write a word equation for the reaction that happens. [2]

....

(e) When a piece of lithium is placed into a gas jar of bromine gas, a similar reaction occurs and a different white solid salt is made. Would this reaction be faster or slower than when Alex performed the experiment with lithium and chlorine? Explain your answer. [2]

....

....

(f) Jess suggests to Alex that they could investigate the reactivity of halogens by seeing which halogens displace other halogens from solutions of their salts. Jess and Alex perform a series of experiments in which they bubble halogen gases through a solution of different potassium halide salts. They record their observations in a table which is shown below.

Element	Potassium Chlorine Solution	Potassium Bromide Solution	Potassium Iodide Solution
Chlorine	No reaction seen	Solution turns brown	Solution turns brown
Bromine	No reaction seen	No reaction seen	Solution turns brown
Iodine	No reaction seen	No reaction seen	No reaction seen

(i) Complete the following word equation. [2]

Chlorine + Potassium bromide ⟶ .... + ...

(ii) Which is the most reactive halogen in this experiment? Put a ring around the correct answer. [1]

Chlorine   Bromine   Iodine

7. The table below shows some information about the electron configurations of some atoms and the ions that they form.

Element	Group Number	Number of Electrons in Atom	Electron Configuration of Atom	Electron Configuration of Ion	Charge on Ion
Lithium	1	3	2.1	2	+1
Sodium	1	11		2.8	+1
Potassium	1	19	2.8.8.1	2.8.8	+1
Magnesium	2	12	2.8.2	2.8	+2
Calcium	2	20	2.8.8.2	2.8.8	+2
Fluorine	7	9	2.7	2.8	−1
Chlorine	7	17	2.8.7	2.8.8	−1
Oxygen	6	8	2.6	2.8	−2

(a) How many electrons does an atom of fluorine have in its outer shell? [1]

....

(b) State the electron configuration of a sodium atom. [1]

....

(c) Strontium is an element in Group 2.

(i) Suggest how many electrons strontium has in the outer shell of its atoms. [1]

....

(ii) Explain your answer to part (i). [1]

....

(d) From the table, name a metal and a non-metal which form ions that have the same electron configuration. [1]

.... and ....

(e) Sulfur is a non-metal element in Group 6 and aluminium is a metal element in Group 3. Suggest what the charge will be on a sulfide ion and an aluminium ion. Explain your answer.

🖉 *The quality of written communication will be assessed in your answer to this question.* [6]

8. This question is about the periodic table.

(a) Which scientists were involved in developing the periodic table? Put ticks (✓) in the boxes next to the **three** correct answers. [3]

Plato	☐	Einstein	☐	Mendeleev	☐
Döbereiner	☐	Newlands	☐	Darwin	☐

(b) The diagram shows a simplified version of the periodic table.

						H											He
Li	Be											B	C	N	O	F	Ne
Na	Mg											Al	Si	P	S	Cl	Ar
K	Ca	Sc	Ti	V	Cr	Mn	Fe	Co	Ni	Cu	Zn	Ga	Ge	As	Se	Br	Kr
Rb	Sr	Y	Zr	Nb	Mo	Tc	Ru	Rh	Pd	Ag	Cd	In	Sn	Sb	Te	I	Xe
Cs	Ba	La*	Hf	Ta	W	Re	Os	Ir	Pt	Au	Hg	Tl	Pb	Bi	Po	At	Rn
Fr	Ra	Ac*	Rf	Db	Sg	Bh	Hs	Mt	Ds	Rg							

(i) What is a horizontal row in the periodic table called? [1]

(ii) What is the name given to the elements in the shaded area? [1]

(c) Draw straight lines to show the correct name for Groups 1, 7 and 0. [3]

Group   **Name**

Group
Group 1

| Group 7 |

| Group 0 |

Name
Halogens

| Alkali metals |

| Noble gases |

| Alkaline earth metals |

9. **(a)** Describe how the ions are arranged in an ionic solid. You can answer the question using a diagram. [2]

(b) Describe what happens to the ions when an ionic solid is melted or dissolved. [1]

(c) Explain why ionic compounds do not conduct electricity when they are solid but do conduct electricity when they are molten or dissolved. [2]

(d) Using the diagram, explain what happens when lithium atoms form ionic bonds with fluorine atoms. Using ideas about stable electron configurations, explain why lithium and fluorine bond in this way.

✎ *The quality of written communication will be assessed in your answer to this question.* [6]

(e) Draw a dot-cross diagram similar to the one in part **(d)** to show ionic bonding between magnesium and oxygen. Remember that the metal atoms lose all their outer shell electrons and the non-metal atoms gain enough electrons to fill their outer shell. [2]

[Total: .... / 95]

Higher Tier

10. Use the periodic table on page 113 to help you to answer this question. Complete the table by working out the missing numbers of protons, electrons and neutrons in the following elements. [4]

Element	Number of Protons	Number of Electrons	Number of Neutrons
Lithium	3	3	4
Fluorine		9	
Aluminium	13	13	
Phosphorus	15		16

11. When potassium reacts with water, potassium hydroxide (KOH) and hydrogen gas are produced. Write a balanced symbol equation to show this. Include state symbols. [3]

12. (a) Explain why all Group 1 elements have similar chemical properties. [2]

(b) Explain why potassium is more reactive than sodium. [2]

13. State and explain the trend in reactivity in the halogens. [3]

14. (a) Looking at the diagrams, how many sodium ions and chloride ions would be needed to form a neutral compound of sodium chloride? Put a tick (✓) in the box next to the correct answer. [1]

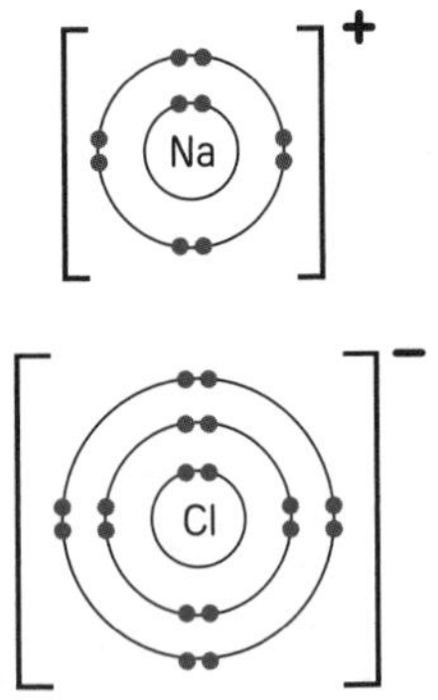

One of each (NaCl) ☐

Two sodium ions and one chloride ion (Na_2Cl) ☐

One sodium ion and two chloride ions ($NaCl_2$) ☐

(b) If magnesium atoms form stable Mg^{2+} ions and oxygen atoms form stable O^{2-} ions, what will be the formulae of the following compounds?

(i) Magnesium oxide _____ [1]

(ii) Magnesium chloride _____ [1]

(iii) Sodium oxide _____ [1]

(c) Given that the formula of an oxide of iron is Fe_2O_3 and the charge on an oxide ion is O^{2-}, work out the charge on the iron ion in this compound. [1]

(d) Strontium oxide has the formula SrO. What is the charge on the strontium ion? Explain your answer using ideas about the periodic table and electron configurations.

✏ *The quality of written communication will be assessed in your answer to this question.* [6]

[Total: _____ / 25]

1. **(a)** Draw straight lines to show the correct definitions of atmosphere, lithosphere and hydrosphere.   [2]

Word	Definition
Atmosphere	The Earth's crust and the solid outer part of the mantle
Lithosphere	The mixture of gases that surrounds the Earth
Hydrosphere	The Earth's oceans, lakes, aquifers, seas and rivers

(b) Complete the following table to show the amount of each gas in clean, dry atmospheric air.   [4]

Gas	Formula	Percentage in Atmosphere
Nitrogen	N_2	78
Oxygen		
Carbon dioxide		0.04
Argon (and other gases)		The rest

(c) Complete the following paragraph. Use words from this list.   [5]

carbon dioxide   electricity   heat
nitrogen   sound   strong   weak

The atmosphere is made from a mixture of gases. Some are elements, including oxygen, argon

and .... Other gases are compounds, including .... These

substances all have low melting and boiling points because they are made from small molecules

with very .... forces of attraction between the molecules. Most of the gases in the

atmosphere are made from molecules but argon is made from single atoms. Atoms in molecules

are joined by covalent bonds. These bonds are very .... Molecular substances do

not conduct .... because their molecules are not charged.

2. The table below shows data on seven different chemicals. Some of these are found in the atmosphere, some are found in the hydrosphere and some are found in the lithosphere.

Substance	Melting Point (°C)	Boiling Point (°C)	State at Room Temperature	Does it Conduct as a Solid?	Does it Conduct as a Liquid or Solution?
A	801	1413	Solid	No	Yes
B	0	100	Liquid	No	No
C	-78	-78	Gas	No	No
D	1650	2230	Solid	No	No
E	2072	2977	Solid	No	Yes
F	-210	-196	Gas	No	No
G	1064	2856	Solid	Yes	Yes

(a) Which of the substances is a metal? [1]

....

(b) Which **two** substances are found in the atmosphere? [2]

.... and ....

(c) Which of the substances is water? [1]

....

(d) Which **two** substances are ionic? [2]

.... and ....

(e) Sometimes when a solid is heated, instead of melting it undergoes a process called **sublimation** in which the solid turns straight into a gas without forming a liquid first.

  (i) Suggest which substance from the table does this. [1]

....

  (ii) Explain your answer to part **(i)**. [1]

....

(f) Silicon dioxide is the main compound in sand. Silicon dioxide has a giant covalent structure, similar to diamond. Its properties are similar to diamond as well. Suggest which of the substances is silicon dioxide. [1]

3. **(a)** What is an ion? [1]

(b) Look at the diagram of part of a crystal of an ionic compound.

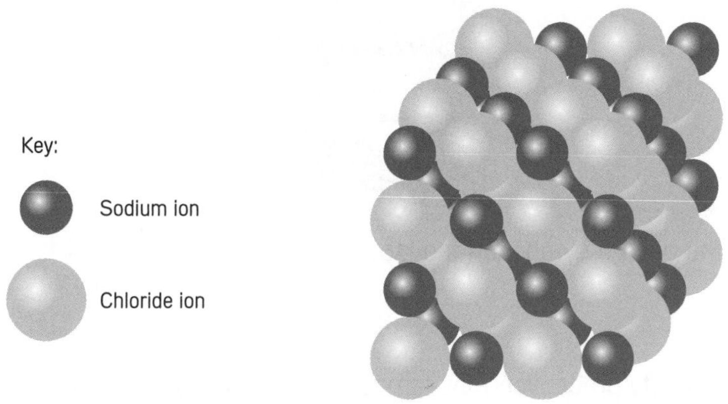

Key:

● Sodium ion

○ Chloride ion

(i) Describe how the ions are arranged. [1]

(ii) What holds the ions together? [1]

(c) Describe and explain the typical properties of ionic compounds.

✎ *The quality of written communication will be assessed in your answer to this question.* [6]

4. James is investigating a compound called zinc chloride.

(a) This is the container that contains the zinc chloride.

(i) What does the hazard symbol on the label mean? [1]

....

(ii) Suggest one safety precaution that James should follow when using zinc chloride. [1]

....

James sets up the apparatus in the diagram below.

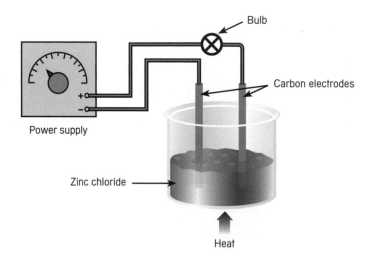

When James switches on the power supply, the bulb does not light at first. However, as he heats the zinc chloride, the bulb lights. James asks his friends to explain what he has seen.

Matthew
The liquid is conducting because it contains a metal.

Sarah
The zinc ions and the chloride ions are now free to move.

Deborah
Carbon conducts electricity so the bulb lights.

Martin
Hot substances conduct electricity better than cold substances.

(b) Which of James' friends has correctly explained why the bulb lights? [1]

....

(c) James continues to heat the zinc chloride in order to keep it molten. He leaves the power supply turned on. After a while, James notices a smell coming from the experiment. It smells of swimming pools and household bleach.

(i) What is the gas that James can smell? [1]

....

(ii) At which electrode will this gas be produced? Put a (ring) around the correct answer. [1]

Positive anode   **Negative cathode**

(d) Gill performs a similar experiment but she uses lead bromide instead of zinc chloride. Complete the table to suggest what is produced at each electrode. [2]

	Positive Anode	**Negative Cathode**
Gill's observations	Brown gas	Bead of molten metal in bottom of electrolyte
Element produced	....	....

5. This question is about some of the gases that are present in the atmosphere.

(a) Draw straight lines to join the name of the gas to its formula and to the correct structure. One has been done for you. [4]

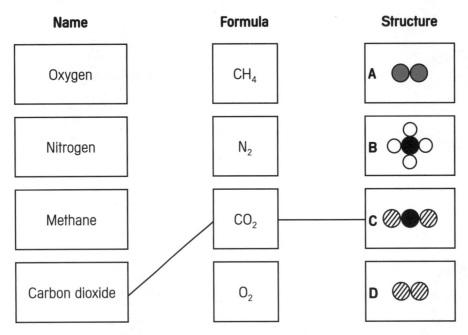

| Name | Formula | Structure |

(b) Here are some statements about the atmosphere. Put a tick (✓) in the correct box to show whether each statement is **true** or **false**. [3]

	true	false
The atmosphere contains mainly ionic substances.	☐	☐
The most abundant gas in the atmosphere is nitrogen.	☐	☐
The amount of carbon dioxide in the atmosphere is less than 1%.	☐	☐

6. **(a)** Complete the following paragraph. Use words from this list. [4]

silicon   **oxygen**   **graphite**   **aluminium**   **crust**

The lithosphere is the outer part of the Earth. It is made from the .... and the solid,

outermost part of the mantle. The lithosphere is made from a mixture of minerals. Two pure forms

(allotropes) of carbon can be found in the lithosphere. They are diamond and ....

Other elements that are very common in the lithosphere are .... ,

.... and oxygen. Much of the silicon and aluminium present in the lithosphere is

chemically bonded to ....

(b) The diagrams show two pure forms of carbon. Label them with their correct names. [2]

(i) ....   **(ii)** ....

 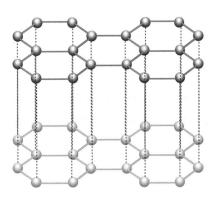

(c) What type of chemical bond joins the carbon atoms together in diamond? [1]

....

(d) State and explain whether diamond has a high or a low melting point and whether or not it conducts electricity.

✎ *The quality of written communication will be assessed in your answer to this question.* [6]

....

....

....

....

....

....

....

....

(e) Describe how the structure of graphite is different from the structure of diamond. [2]

....

....

....

(f) Explain why graphite has a very high melting point. [3]

....

....

....

(g) Graphite is very unusual in that it is one of a very small number of covalently bonded non-metal substances that can conduct electricity. Explain how it can do this. [3]

....

....

....

7. Here is a diagram of silicon dioxide.

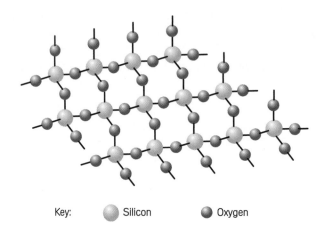

Key: ⬤ Silicon ⬤ Oxygen

Use your understanding of how bonding and structure determine the properties of a substance to predict and explain the following properties of silicon dioxide.

(a) Melting point: .... [2]

....

(b) Hardness: .... [2]

....

(c) Electrical conductivity: .... [3]

....

8. Complete the following paragraph using the words below. [4]

reduction   **oxygen**   **redox**   **electrolysis**   **gold**

The lithosphere contains many types of rock, including some that contain minerals from which metals

can be economically extracted. These rocks are called ores. Some of the metals are very valuable so

it is worth mining and purifying large quantities of ore to extract a small amount of metal. Many ores

contain metal elements that are bonded to .... This must be removed in a process

that is the opposite to oxidation, called .... Many less reactive metals can be reduced

by heating them with carbon, which reacts with the oxygen and removes it. The carbon is therefore

oxidised while the metal is reduced. When oxidation and reduction take place at the same time, we call

the overall process .... More reactive metals must be reduced using a process called

............................., in which electricity is used to split up a dissolved or molten ionic compound. The

least reactive metals, such as ...., do not easily react with oxygen so they are found

pure in the lithosphere.

9. **(a)** Use the periodic table on page 113 to write down the relative atomic masses of the following elements.

     (i) Iron: .... [1]

     (ii) Copper: .... [1]

     (iii) Oxygen: .... [1]

   (b) Work out the relative formula mass of the following compounds.

     (i) CuO: .... [1]

     (ii) Fe_3O_4: .... [1]

10. Aluminium is extracted from aluminium oxide by electrolysis.

(a) Label the following diagram using the words below. [3]

Carbon anode **Cathode** **Electrolyte** **Aluminium siphoned off**

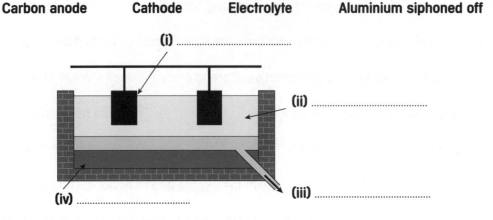

(i) ....

(ii) ....

(iii) ....

(iv) ....

(b) Describe what happens to the aluminium ions (Al^{3+}) and the oxide ions (O^{2-}) when the solid aluminium oxide dissolves into the electrolyte. [1]

....

....

(c) Describe and explain what happens to the aluminium ions during the electrolysis of molten aluminium oxide. [2]

....

....

....

(d) Describe and explain what happens to the oxide ions during the electrolysis of molten aluminium oxide. [2]

....

....

....

OCR Twenty First Century GCSE
Additional Science A Workbook Answers

Answering Quality of Written Communication Questions

A number of the questions in your examinations will include an assessment of the quality of your written communication (QWC). These questions are worth a maximum of 6 marks and are indicated by a pencil icon (✐).

Your answers to these questions will be marked according to...
- the level of your understanding of the relevant science
- how well you structure your answer
- the style of your writing, including the quality of your punctuation, grammar and spelling.

QWC questions will be marked using a 'Levels of Response' mark scheme. The examiner will decide whether your answer is in the top level, middle level or bottom level. The expected quality of written communication is different in the three levels and it will always be considered at the same time as looking at the scientific information in your answer:
- To achieve Level 3 (which is the top level and is worth 5–6 marks), your answer should contain relevant science, and be organised and presented in a structured and coherent manner. You should use scientific terms appropriately and your spelling, punctuation and grammar should have very few errors.
- For Level 2 (worth 3–4 marks), there may be more errors in your spelling, punctuation and grammar, and your answer will miss some of the things expected at Level 3.

- For Level 1 (worth 1–2 marks), your answer may be written using simplistic language. You will have included some relevant science, but the quality of your written communication may have limited how well the examiner can understand your answer. This could be due to lots of errors in spelling, punctuation and grammar, misuse of scientific terms or a poor structure.
- An answer given Level 0 may contain insufficient or irrelevant science, and will not be given any marks.

You will be awarded the higher or lower mark within a particular level depending on the quality of the science and the quality of the written communication in your answer.

Even if the quality of your written communication is perfect, the level you are awarded will be limited if you show little understanding of the relevant science, and you will be given Level 0 if you show no relevant scientific understanding at all.

To help you understand the criteria above, three specimen answers are provided to the first QWC question in this workbook. The first is a model answer worth 6 marks, the second answer would be worth 4 marks and the third answer worth 2 marks. The three exemplar answers are differentiated by their scientific content and use of scientific terminology. Model answers worth 6 marks are provided to all other QWC questions to help you aspire to the best possible marks.

Module B4: The Processes of Life
(Pages 4–14)

1. B

2. protein **should be ringed**.

3. (a) The enzyme does not work / is denatured / is destroyed (at high temperatures) **[1]**. The active site / shape of the enzyme is changed; The active site / shape of the enzyme no longer fits the starch molecule (so the starch is not broken down / stays intact) **[1]. [No marks for 'The enzyme is killed'.]**
    (b) To make sure her results were repeatable, so that any difference was caused by the change in temperature. **[No marks for references to a 'fair test'.]**
    (c) **This is a model answer which would score full marks:** Chloe would need to use a minimum of five different samples of protein. She would then add a set amount of pepsin to the protein. She would need to keep the temperature and pH the same for each treatment. After a set time she would determine how much of the protein had been broken down. By repeating the experiment at a range of temperatures, she would be able to work out the optimum temperature for pepsin. The experiment would not work with starch because pepsin is an enzyme that is specific for protein. Starch is a carbohydrate and so would not be affected at all by pepsin. **This answer would score 4 marks:** Chloe should use a range of at least five different temperatures. At each one she should add the same amounts of pepsin and protein together, keeping everything else the same. The temperature at which the protein was broken down the fastest would be the best temperature for pepsin to work at. She could not use starch for this, as it is not a protein. It would not be affected at all, as pepsin only works on protein, and not on anything else. **This answer would score 2 marks:** Chloe should carry out an experiment adding the same amounts of pepsin and protein together each time. She could then find out which

temperature is the quickest for the pepsin to break down the protein. The pepsin would not work on starch, as it is not a protein.

4. **This is a model answer which would score full marks:** The cytoplasm is where anaerobic respiration occurs and where the enzymes needed for it are made. Aerobic respiration occurs in the mitochondria and the enzymes needed for it are made in these. The energy released by both anaerobic and aerobic respiration may be used for synthesising large molecules, such as polymers like proteins. It may be used as the activation energy for other cell processes, such as active transport.

5. (a) Carbon dioxide; Oxygen (b) Chlorophyll
    (c) **Any one from:** It will not grow as much; It will go yellow; It will grow tall and skinny.

6. (a) 18
    (b) **Any two from:** The number of buttercups increases the further away from the trees; The number of buttercups increases steadily to 4–6 metres; The number of buttercups levels off beyond the 6-metre mark.
    (c) To increase the repeatability / reliability of the data / results.

7. **This is a model answer which would score full marks:** Seedlings A and C grew a lot in the warm places. Seedling D had grown a little and the shaded windowsill would not have been as warm as seedling A's windowsill. Seedling B had not grown at all in the cold. From these observations, Petra would have been right. However, seedlings C and D were both healthy-looking and had been exposed to light. Seedling A was looking very thin and yellow. Seedling B had not changed at all, so being in the dark had not caused it to grow. From these observations, Petra was wrong. Overall, based on her evidence, Petra could not make a firm conclusion as to whether it was light or temperature that had caused the differences. She would have to do more and improved experiments in order to establish this.

8. **(a)** Glucose + Oxygen ⟶ Carbon dioxide + Water (+ Energy)
   [1 for correct reactants; 1 for correct products]
   (b) **Any two from:** Anaerobic respiration does not need oxygen; Anaerobic respiration produces lactic acid; Anaerobic respiration produces less energy (per glucose molecule). **Or any two from:** Aerobic respiration needs oxygen; Aerobic respiration does not produce lactic acid; Aerobic respiration produces more energy (per glucose molecule).
   (c) (i) Enzyme
   (ii) **Any one from:** Protein; Amino acids

9. **(a) (i)** B
   (ii) A
   (iii) E
   (b) **Any two from:** Bacterial cells do not have a nucleus, whereas animal cells do have a nucleus; Bacterial cells have no mitochondria, whereas animal cells do have mitochondria; Bacterial cells have a protein / non-cellulose cell wall, unlike animal cells; Bacterial cells have plasmids / a circle of DNA, unlike animal cells.

10. **(a)** Fresh pineapple juice has something in it that makes the jelly disappear.
    (b) Tube A acts as a control / acts as a comparison / shows that other liquids / water do not affect the jelly.
    (c) (i) **Any one from:** Enzymes; Proteases
    (ii) **Any one from:** Destroyed it; Denatured it; Changed it; Stopped it working
    [No marks for 'Killed it'.]
    (d) The jelly would have disappeared more quickly in tube B **[1]** because there would be a greater surface area of jelly touching the pineapple juice **[1]**.

11. **(a)** Because it comes from living organisms
    (b) Because the bacteria respire anaerobically
    (c) Methane
    (d) **Any two from:** There is no need to dispose of the waste products it is made from in landfill sites; It does not add to acid rain / sulfur dioxide; It is carbon neutral / the carbon dioxide produced is balanced by crops planted to produce more biofuel; It reduces use of fossil fuels; It reduces the need to transport fuels around the world; It reduces pollution from oil spills, etc.; It is a renewable fuel.

12. **(a)** Carbon dioxide
    (b) Because the yeast will respire aerobically / with oxygen **[1]** and ethanol / alcohol production needs anaerobic conditions / no oxygen **[1]**.
    (c) It is needed for (both aerobic and anaerobic) respiration to take place.

13. Emily; Darren

14. **(a)** So that there would be no photosynthesis occurring **[1]** and any food reserves / starch in the leaf would be used up **[1]**.
    (b) In the inner / green part **[1]** because there is / are no chlorophyll / chloroplasts in the white part / no photosynthesis takes place / no light is absorbed in the white part **[or reverse if referring to the green part]** **[1]**.

15. **This is a model answer which would score full marks:** As well as the correct temperature, plants need carbon dioxide and light for photosynthesis. If there is a lack of carbon dioxide in the greenhouse, then carbon dioxide becomes a limiting factor. Burning wood makes more carbon dioxide available for photosynthesis. For example, the greenhouse may have 1 arbitrary unit of carbon dioxide, whilst burning wood may bring the level up to 4 arbitrary units, which means the plants have enough carbon dioxide for growth. However, smoke from the burning wood may end up blocking the light in the greenhouse, so then light becomes a limiting factor.

16. $6CO_2$; $6O_2$ **[1 for correct symbols; 1 for correctly balancing]**

17. **(a)** **Any one from:** Yes because the reaction happens most quickly at pH 1; No because there is no result for pH 2 or

pH 3, so it is not possible to tell if the reaction would happen more quickly at these pH values.
   (b) **This is a model answer which would score full marks:** Enzymes have a specific shape that enables a specific substrate to fit into it, which then allows the reaction to take place. This is called the lock-and-key hypothesis. The enzyme is the lock and the substrate is the key. Denaturing is where an enzyme undergoes a permanent change in shape. It can be caused by high temperature or the incorrect pH. Once the enzyme has denatured, the substrate no longer fits into the lock and so the reaction cannot take place. In humans the stomach is at pH 1, so pepsin works best at this pH. If it did not, it would be inefficient.

18. **(a)** Osmosis
    (b) Active transport
    (c) Mitochondria are sites of aerobic respiration / provide energy for the process.

19. The movement of water from a dilute solution to a more concentrated solution **should be ticked**.

20. **(a)** $C_6H_{12}O_6 + 6O_2 \longrightarrow 6CO_2 + 6H_2O$ (+ Energy)
    [1 for correct reactants; 1 for correct products; 1 for correctly balancing]
    (b) Root cells can respire anaerobically / without oxygen.

21. **(a)** The potato took in water **[1]** because the solution inside its cells was more concentrated than the solution outside **[1]**.
    (b) The potato lost water **[1]** because the solution outside its cells was more concentrated than the solution inside **[1]**.

Module B5: Growth and Development (Pages 15–25)

1. **Lines should be drawn from** Egg **to** A female gamete; **from** Fertilisation **to** The fusion of a male gamete with a female gamete; **from** Sperm **to** A male gamete.

2. **(a)** Mitosis
   (b) So that the zygote / fertilised egg will end up with a whole set of chromosomes.

3. **(a)** Embryonic stem cells can be used to form any cell type **[1]**, whereas adult stem cells will only produce cells of a certain type **[1]**.
   (b) 8 cell stage **should be ringed**.
   (c) They start to become specialised.

4. Salivary amylase production **and** Membrane protein formation **should be ticked**.

5. **(a)** To replace damaged tissues
   (b) Adult stem cells

6. **(a)** mitosis **should be ringed**.
   (b) **Any suitable answers, e.g.** Plants continue to grow in height and width throughout their lives, whereas animals only grow in the early stages of their lives; Plants only grow at root / shoot tips, whereas animals grow in all areas of the body.

7. **(a)** **Any one from:** By being able to grow towards the source of light, the plants would be able to ensure the maximum light levels **[1]**, and grow well **[1]**; If the plants grew away from the light rather than towards it, they would not get enough light **[1]**, and would die **[1]**.
   (b) Shoot D
   (c) Direction of sunlight

8. **(a)** **Any one from:** A; D
   (b) 23 **should be ringed**.

9. The parent cell divides by meiosis to form gametes **[1]**. Gametes from the male and female fuse during fertilisation **[1]**. Cells in the zygote divide by mitosis **[1]**.

10. double; base; gene; protein

11. **(a)** To ensure she could obtain repeatable results **[1]** and be certain that any difference was due to temperature only **[1]**. **[No marks for references to a 'fair test'.]**

(b) The results up to 40°C did show an increase in cloudiness as the temperature increased.

(c) No. The broth still went slightly cloudy at 50°C, so there was still evidence of growth at that temperature.

(d) Yes. He could measure a difference numerically, rather than just through an observation.

12. **(a)** Mitosis
(b) Meristems
(c) If a cell is unspecialised, it has not yet developed into a particular type of cell.
(d) Because all the cells are unspecialised **[1]**, so they can develop into all the different types of plant cell needed **[1]**.

13. Plant B has a longer stem to try to find light more quickly **[1]**. It has a bent stem in response to gravity / because the shoot grows upwards / against gravity **[1]**.

14. **(a)** Zygote
(b) Meiosis
(c) Mitosis
(d) (Embryonic) stem cells

15. **(a)** Mitosis
(b) Meiosis
(c) Because they are gametes / sex cells / need to have half the chromosome number of the parent cell.

16. Amanda; Miriam

17. **(a) (i)** A tissue is a group of similar cells that carry out a particular function.
(ii) Any suitable example, e.g. Cornea; Leaf epidermis; Palisade layer; Heart muscle
(b) (i) An organ is a group of tissues that carry out a particular function.
(ii) Any suitable example, e.g. Heart; Lungs; Leaf; Tree trunk; Stomach

18. **This is a model answer which would score full marks:**
Embryonic stem cells can become any type of cell. Treating a patient with Parkinson's disease using embryonic stem cells means that the cells damaged by Parkinson's disease can be replaced with functioning ones. The treatment is used to minimise the suffering of a human being. Embryonic stem cells are harvested from embryos. Some people view these embryos as being people. They would argue that it is wrong to stop an embryo from growing in order to save the life of another. Scientists are developing techniques that enable adult cells to have the same ability as embryonic stem cells. This would mean the issue of using embryonic stem cells is removed.

19. **(a)** DNA has four bases: A, C, G and T **[1]**. These bases always pair A with T and C with G **[1]**. The order of these bases in the DNA strand is the genetic code for building up proteins from amino acids **[1]**.
(b) A stomach cell will make pepsin because the base sequence **[1]** for this protein is switched on **[1]**. A skin cell has this sequence switched off, so it will not make pepsin **[1]**.

20. **(a) (i)** **The drawing needs to show a straight, taller shoot [1] with dots evenly spread on both sides of the shoot [1].**
(ii) **The drawing needs to show the shoot curving towards the light [1] with dots on the left-hand side of the shoot (i.e. the side furthest away from the light) [1].**
(b) **The drawing needs to show a straight, taller shoot [1] with an opaque cap over the shoot tip [1].**
(c) Any two from: The plant will grow towards the light **[1]** so it can photosynthesise more / make more food / glucose **[1]** for growth / fruit / seed development **[1]**.

21. The cell contains all the genetic material / code / DNA / genes **[1]**, so the genes for all the different types of cell are available in a body cell **[1]**.

22. **(a)** The order of the bases
(b) Enzymes

23. **(a)** Root hormone
(b) They affect cell division **[1]** at the tip of a shoot and/or root **[1]** and cause cells to grow in size **[1]**.
(c) They are genetically identical.

Module B6: Brain and Mind (Pages 26–37)

1. **(a)** Stimulus **should be ticked**.
(b) (i) A reflex
(ii) They are more likely to survive.
(c) The Royal Mail delivery truck is red.
(d) **This is a model answer which would score full marks:**
Fiesa would introduce objects that are red, as well as other colours, to a number of territorial sticklebacks in fish tanks. Each non-red object would have to be the same size and shape as the red object. Fiesa would then count how often the territorial stickleback attacked each object that was introduced in the fish tank. She would repeat the experiment with each stickleback. She would then see if the number of times the red object was attacked was significantly higher than the attacks on the non-red objects.

2. **(a)** Reflexes of newborn babies
(b) Any one from: The lower the birth weight, the lower the chance of passing the test; The greater the birth weight, the greater the chance of passing the test.
(c) Step: The baby will make stepping motions when the sole of its foot touches a hard surface.
Grasp: The baby will grasp and hold tight a finger placed into its palm.
Startle: The baby pulls arms and legs inward after loud noise.
(d) 0.29 × 340 = 98.6
98.6 is rounded up to 99.
[1 mark for correct working; 2 marks for 99 with or without working; 1 mark only for 98.6]
(e) Any one from: Pupil reflex; Knee jerk; Dropping a hot object
(f) Electrical
(g) Hormones are chemical, whereas nerve signals are electrical; Hormone messages are slow, whereas nerve signals are fast; Hormone messages are long-lasting, whereas nerve signals are short-lived.

3. **(a)** **Lines should be drawn from** Receptor **to** Sensory neuron **to** Relay neuron **to** Motor neuron **to** Effector. **[1 for two correct lines; 2 for all correct]**
(b) A reflex arc
(c) (i) 0.9–3.1s
(ii) She added up nine of the numbers (ignoring test 8) **[1]** and divided the total by nine **[1]**.
(d) As the test number increases, the time taken to catch the £10 note decreases.

4. **(a)**

A	C	B	D

[Accept 'C' before 'A']
(b) This is the same experiment that Pavlov undertook **and** Humans are also animals **should be ticked. [Both needed for 1 mark.]**

5. **(a)** The nerve signals cannot travel past the break in the cord.
(b) The sample size for this experiment is one **and** The mechanism behind the experiment is not understood **should be ticked. [Both needed for 1 mark.]**

6. **(a)** **A scatter graph should be plotted as follows: Neuron Diameter should be on the x-axis and Speed of Nerve Impulse on the y-axis [1]; All points should be accurately plotted [1]; A line of best fit (not joined dot-to-dot) should be drawn on the graph [1].**

(b) The greater the diameter of the neuron, the faster the impulse.

(c) A fatty sheath **should be ticked**.

7. **(a)** billions **should be ringed**.
    (b) It increases
    (c) **(i)** By having a new experience
        (ii) By the experience being repeated
        (iii) They are deleted
    (d) Every time an experience is repeated, the neuron pathways are strengthened **[1]**. These pathways are more likely to transmit impulses, so you will learn how to do a task **[1]**.

8. **(a)** Physiological techniques study the effects of damage to different parts of the brain **[1]** in order to understand which parts of the brain control different functions **[1]**.
    (b) Magnetic Resonance Imaging (MRI) scanning
    (c) **(i)** The activities use different parts of the brain **should be ticked**.
        (ii) It prevents the scientists from introducing bias. They may be looking for evidence that the patient has responded 'yes' or 'no' where none exists.

9. **(a)** Group 1 **[1]**. The numbers have a clear pattern with group 1 **[1]** and there is no distraction to the process of remembering **[1]**.
    (b) **Any one from:** Remembering numbers is easiest if there is a pattern and no distractions; Remembering is most difficult when there is no pattern and there are distractions.
    (c) **Any one from:** Participants should be the same age / in the same age group; Participants should be the same sex; The tests should be carried out at the same time of day for each group.
    (d) The success rate of the groups should improve **[1]**. Over time they would adapt to the noise **[1]**.
    (e) It would enable the parts of the brain involved in memorising numbers **[1]** and coping with loud music to be identified **[1]**.

10. Insulin needs to affect the whole body but a nervous impulse does not affect the whole body **[1]**. The response needs to be long-term but nervous responses are short-term **[1]**.

11. **(a)** **This is a model answer which would score full marks:**
    Taste buds are spread all over the tongue and are the receptors that detect stimuli. The stimuli for the taste buds are the chemical taste particles that land on the taste bud when food substances are placed in the mouth. Each taste bud contains specialised cells with microvilli, which respond to the five different tastes. Sensory neurons send an electrical nerve impulse to the brain, where it is processed and interpreted. The person then perceives the taste as being either one taste or a combination of the five tastes – sweet, salty, bitter, sour and umami.
    (b) The tongue map idea was powerful and difficult to counter **and** The modern research took place a long time after the original research **should be ticked**.
    (c) Actual quantities could not be measured **[1]**. This meant that there was only a relative (proportional) indication of taste detection **[1]**.

12. **(a)**

C	E	A	D	B

[2 for all correct; 1 for three letters in the correct sequence]
    (b) **(i)** Ecstasy / MDMA **[accept 'Prozac']**
        (ii) The sites where serotonin is reabsorbed into the sensory neuron are blocked.
        (iii) The nerve impulses would travel faster because the serotonin remains in the synapse.
    (c) Michael

13. **(a)** The benefit to the patient outweighs the risk of the operation **should be ticked**.
    (b) Her brain used different neuron pathways to carry out tasks.

Module C4: Chemical Patterns (Pages 38–48)

1. **(a)** Richard
    (b) James
    (c) Hydrogen
    (d) **Any one from:** Yes, because the reaction has been filmed and is therefore reliable evidence; No, because the reaction might have been faked.

2. **(a)**

	Mass	Charge	Where in the Atom is it Found?
Proton	1	**Positive**	In the nucleus
Electron	Approx. 0	Negative	Orbiting the nucleus
Neutron	1	**No charge**	**In the nucleus**

    (b) Neutral **[1]** because every atom has the same number of positive protons and negative electrons **[1]**.
    (c) two; eight; eight **['18' is also acceptable.]**
    (d) **(i)** 2.4
        (ii) 2.8.7
        (iii) 2.8.1
        (iv) 2.8.8.1
    (e) The group number is the number of electrons in the outer shell.
    (f) The period number is the number of full or partially-filled electron shells.
    (g) Silicon

3. **(a)** colour / frequency / wavelength **[1]**; spectroscopy **[1]**; spectrum **[1]**
    (b) **This is a model answer which would score full marks:**
    Take a nichrome wire loop. Clean it by dipping in acid and then heating it in a blue Bunsen flame. Use the loop to pick up a few crystals of the solid to be tested and place it into the blue Bunsen flame. Record the colour of the flame and compare it with known samples or a reliable reference such as a textbook. **[An answer which states using a splint instead of a wire loop would also be acceptable.]**

4. **(a)** **Lines should be drawn from the first symbol to** Corrosive; **from the second symbol to** Flammable; **from the third symbol to** Oxidising agent **and from the fourth symbol to** Harmful. **[1 for each correct line up to a maximum of 3.]**
    (b) **Any one from:** Turn off Bunsen burner; Keep away from hot objects; Keep away from sources of ignition
    (c) **Any two from:** Wear gloves; Wear goggles; Wear a lab coat

5. **(a)** **Any four from:** Li; Na; K; Rb; Cs; Fr **[Four needed for 1 mark.]**
    (b) Alkali metals
    (c) To prevent them from reacting with (oxygen or moisture in) the air.
    (d)

Element	Melting Point (K)	Boiling Point (K)	Formula of Chloride
Lithium	453	**Any answer greater than 1250**	LiCl
Sodium	370	1156	**NaCl**
Potassium	**Any answer less than 350**	1032	KCl

    (e) **Any two from:** The sodium floats; It fizzes; It moves around on the surface; It gets smaller.
    (f) **(i)** Lithium + Water $\longrightarrow$ Lithium hydroxide + Hydrogen **[1 for correct reactants; 1 for correct products]**
        (ii) Sodium + Chlorine $\longrightarrow$ Sodium chloride **[1 for correct reactants; 1 for correct product, correctly spelt]**
    (g) It increases
    (h) **Any one from:** It will react violently; It will explode; The reaction will be faster than with potassium.
    (i) **Any answer less than 300K.**

6. (a) The halogens **should be ticked**.
   (b) **Diagram C should be ringed**.
   (c)

Element	Formula	Appearance at Room Temperature (colour and state)	Melting Point (K)	Boiling Point (K)
Chlorine	Cl_2	**Green gas**	**Any answer between 100 and 200**	239
Bromine	**Br_2**	Orange / brown liquid, evaporates easily	266	332
Iodine	I_2	Grey solid, sublimes to purple vapour	387	**Any answer between 387 and 400**

   (d) Lithium + Chlorine $\longrightarrow$ Lithium chloride **[1 for correct reactants; 1 for correct product]**
   (e) Slower **[1]** because bromine is less reactive than chlorine **[1]**.
   (f) (i) Potassium chloride; Bromine
       (ii) Chlorine **should be ringed**.

7. (a) Seven
   (b) 2.8.1
   (c) (i) 2
       (ii) **Any one from:** All elements in Group 2 have two electrons in their outer shell; It will follow the pattern seen in magnesium and calcium atoms in the table; The group number is the same as the number of electrons in the outer shell of an atom.
   (d) **Any one pair (both required for 1 mark) from:** Sodium and fluorine; Sodium and oxygen; Magnesium and fluorine; Calcium and chlorine; Potassium and chlorine; Magnesium and oxygen
   (e) **This is a model answer which would score full marks:**
       Sulfur is in Group 6 and therefore has six electrons in its outer shell. It will gain two electrons to achieve a full outer shell, which is a stable electron configuration. Gaining two electrons will give the sulfide ion a charge of 2− (S^{2-}). Aluminium is in Group 3 and therefore has three electrons in its outer shell. It will lose three electrons to achieve an empty (or full) outer shell. Losing three electrons will cause the aluminium ion to have a charge of 3+ (Al^{3+}).

8. (a) Döbereiner, Newlands **and** Mendeleev **should be ticked**.
   (b) (i) A period
       (ii) **Any one from:** The transition metals; The transition elements
   (c) **Lines should be drawn from** Group 1 **to** Alkali metals; **from** Group 7 **to** Halogens **and from** Group 0 **to** Noble gases. **[1 for each correct line.]**

9. (a) Oppositely charged ions **[1]** are arranged in a regular lattice **[1]**. **2 marks can also be obtained by a diagram, e.g.:**

   Key:
   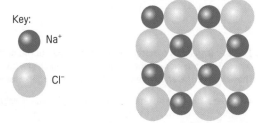
   ● Na^+

   ● Cl^-

   (b) The ions can move freely.
   (c) In a solid, the ions are locked in place **[1]**. In a liquid or solution, the ions are free to move and conduct electricity **[1]**.

   (d) **This is a model answer which would score full marks:**
       One electron from the outer shell of a lithium atom will be transferred to a fluorine atom. This leaves the lithium as a stable positive ion with an empty outer shell and the fluorine as a stable negative ion with a full outer shell. The opposite charges on the lithium (Li^+) and the fluoride (F^-) ions cause them to be strongly attracted and form an ionic lattice.
   (e)

   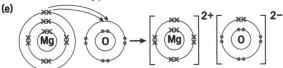

   [1 for correct electron configurations of ions and 1 for correct charges]

10.

Element	Number of Protons	Number of Electrons	Number of Neutrons
Lithium	3	3	4
Fluorine	**9**	9	**10**
Aluminium	13	13	**14**
Phosphorus	15	**15**	16

11. $2K(s) + 2H_2O(l) \longrightarrow 2KOH(aq) + H_2(g)$ **[1 for correct formulae; 1 for balancing correctly; 1 for correct state symbols]**

12. (a) All the Group 1 elements have one electron in their outer shell **[1]**. All the Group 1 elements need to lose one electron to become stable **[1]**.
    (b) Potassium's outer electron is further from its nucleus **[1]** so it is lost more easily **[1]**. **[No marks for 'the outer electron is lost faster'.]**

13. Reactivity decreases as you go down the group **[1]** because the atom gains an electron less easily **[1]**. This is due to the electron going into a shell that is further from the nucleus / the electron being attracted less strongly **[1]**.

14. (a) One of each (NaCl) **should be ticked**.
    (b) (i) MgO
        (ii) $MgCl_2$
        (iii) Na_2O
    (c) Fe^{3+} / positive 3
    (d) **This is a model answer which would score full marks:**
        The strontium ion will have a charge of 2+ (Sr^{2+}). This can be explained in two ways. First, strontium is in Group 2 so its atoms have two electrons in their outer shell. These two outer electrons will be lost during ionic bonding, so the ion will have a charge of 2+. Second, the formula of strontium oxide, SrO, shows that one strontium ion is needed for each oxide ion. Oxygen is in Group 6 so its atoms have six electrons in their outer shell and would need to gain two electrons to become stable ions. The charge on an oxide ion is therefore 2− (O^{2-}), so the charge on a strontium ion would need to be Sr^{2+}.

Module C5: Chemicals of the Natural Environment (Pages 49–63)

1. (a) **Lines should be drawn from** Atmosphere **to** The mixture of gases that surrounds the Earth; **from** Lithosphere **to** The Earth's crust and the solid outer part of the mantle **and from** Hydrosphere **to** The Earth's oceans, lakes, aquifers, seas and rivers. **[1 for each correct line up to a maximum of 2.]**
   (b)

Gas	Formula	Percentage in Atmosphere
Nitrogen	N_2	78
Oxygen	**O_2**	**21**
Carbon dioxide	**CO_2**	0.04
Argon (and other gases)	**Ar**	The rest

   (c) nitrogen; carbon dioxide; weak; strong; electricity

2. **(a)** G
   (b) C; F
   (c) B
   (d) A; E
   (e) (i) C
   (ii) Because it melts and boils at the same temperature (i.e. instantaneously)
   (f) D

3. **(a)** An atom or group of atoms with an electrical charge.
   (b) (i) Any one from: In a regular arrangement; In a lattice
   (ii) Any one from: Electrostatic forces; Attraction between oppositely charged ions
   (c) This is a model answer which would score full marks:
   One typical property of ionic compounds is that they have high melting points. This is because the oppositely charged ions are held together in a lattice by very strong electrostatic forces of attraction which require a lot of energy to break. Another property is that ionic compounds do not conduct electricity when they are solid because the ions are fixed in place. However, when the compound is melted or dissolved, the ions are free to move and so the substance can conduct electricity.

4. **(a) (i)** Corrosive
   (ii) Any one from: Wear gloves; Wear goggles
   (b) Sarah
   (c) (i) Chlorine
   (ii) Positive anode **should be ringed**.
   (d)

	Positive Anode	Negative Cathode
Gill's observations	Brown gas	Bead of molten metal in bottom of electrolyte
Element produced	**Bromine**	**Lead**

5. **(a) Lines should be drawn from** Oxygen to O_2 **and then to** Diagram D; **from** Nitrogen **to** N_2 **and then to** Diagram A **and from** Methane **to** CH_4 **and then to** Diagram B.
   [1 for each correct line linking names and formulae up to a maximum of 2; 1 for each correct line linking formulae and diagrams up to a maximum of 2.]
   (b) The atmosphere contains mainly ionic substances: false; The most abundant gas in the atmosphere is nitrogen: true; The amount of carbon dioxide in the atmosphere is less than 1%: true

6. **(a)** crust; graphite; aluminium; silicon **[these two in any order];** oxygen **[1 for each correct up to a maximum of 4.]**
   (b) (i) Diamond
   (ii) Graphite
   (c) Covalent bond
   (d) This is a model answer which would score full marks:
   The melting point of diamond is very high because it has a giant covalent structure. Each carbon atom is bonded to four other carbon atoms by strong covalent bonds which require a lot of energy to break. There are no delocalised electrons or other charged particles (such as ions) that are free to move, so diamond does not conduct electricity.
   (e) Any two from: Carbon atoms in graphite are bonded in layers; Each carbon atom is bonded to three others, not four as in diamond; There are weak forces between the layers; There are delocalised electrons in graphite.
   (f) Any suitable answer, e.g. Graphite has many **[1]** strong / covalent **[1]** bonds which require a lot of energy **[1]** to break; In graphite each carbon atom is bonded to three other carbon atoms **[1]** by strong / covalent **[1]** bonds which require a lot of energy **[1]** to break.
   (g) Graphite has delocalised electrons **[1]** which are able to move between the layers **[1]** and carry charge **[1]**.

7. **(a)** High melting point **[1]** because **[any one from]** strong / covalent bonds between atoms **[1]** require a lot of energy to break **[1]** like diamond **[1]**.
   (b) Very hard **[1]** because **[any one from]** strong / covalent

bonds between atoms **[1]** require a lot of energy to break **[1]** like diamond **[1]**.
   (c) Will not conduct electricity **[1]** because there are no electrons or ions **[1]** that are able to move **[1]**.

8. oxygen; reduction; redox; electrolysis; gold **[1 for each correct up to a maximum of 4.]**

9. **(a) (i)** 56
   (ii) 63.5
   (iii) 16
   (b) (i) 79.5
   (ii) 232

10. **(a) [1 for each correct up to a maximum of 3.]**
   (i) Carbon anode
   (ii) Electrolyte
   (iii) Aluminium siphoned off
   (iv) Cathode
   (b) The ions become free to move through the electrolyte.
   (c) The Al^{3+} ions move towards the cathode **[1]** because they are attracted to the opposite / negative charge **[1]**.
   (d) The O^{2-} ions move towards the anode **[1]** because they are attracted to the opposite / positive charge **[1]**.

11. **Lines should be drawn from** Copper used for electrical wiring **to** Good electrical conductor **and then to** Delocalised electrons are free to move.
   Lines should be drawn from Aluminium used for saucepans **to** High melting point **and then to** Strong bonds between metal ions take a lot of energy to overcome.
   Lines should be drawn from Steel used for car body panels **to** Malleable and strong **and then to** Strong bonds between metal ions can re-form in a new shape.
   A line should be drawn from Good conductor of heat **to** Close-packed metal ions transfer vibrations effectively.
   [1 for each correct line linking boxes in the first column with boxes in the second column up to a maximum of 2; 1 for each correct line linking boxes in the second column with boxes in the third column up to a maximum of 3.]

12. **(a) Lines should be drawn from** Reusing metals **to** Very little environmental impact; **from** Recycling metals **to** Uses a lot less energy than mining the ore and extracting the metal **and from** Throwing away metals **to** Landfill sites destroy natural habitats and heavy metals can pollute groundwater.
   [1 for each correct line up to a maximum of 2.]
   (b) Any three from: Noise pollution; Increased traffic; Pollution from transport; Dust; Loss of natural habitats; Deforestation; Carbon dioxide emissions from machinery

13. **(a)** The nuclei are both attracted to the electrons **[1]** that are shared in the covalent bond **[1]**.
   (b) They all have a full outer shell.
   (c)

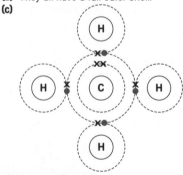

   [1 for four pairs of electrons in the outer shell of the carbon atom; 1 for positioning these four pairs of electrons so that they overlap the shell of each of the four hydrogen atoms.]

14. **(a)** Add sodium hydroxide solution **[1]**. A light blue precipitate identifies copper ions **[1]**.
   $Cu^{2+} + 2OH^- \longrightarrow Cu(OH)_2$ **[1 for correct formulae and charges; 1 for balancing correctly]**
   (b) Carbonate ions are not present; Sulfate ions are present

(c) **This is a model answer which would score full marks:**
Zoe should test to see if the metal ion is iron(II) or iron(III) by adding sodium hydroxide solution. If iron(II) ions are present, Zoe will see a green precipitate. If iron(III) ions are present, Zoe will see a red-brown precipitate. Zoe can distinguish between the chloride, bromide and iodide ions by adding dilute nitric acid and then silver nitrate solution to a new sample of the water. A white precipitate indicates chloride ions are present, a cream precipitate indicates bromide ions are present and a yellow precipitate indicates iodide ions are present.

15. (a) Calcium carbonate
(b) Silver nitrate **[1]** and sodium chloride / sodium carbonate **[1]**
(c) (i) (White) precipitate
(ii) Calcium nitrate + Sodium carbonate $\longrightarrow$ Calcium carbonate + Sodium nitrate **[1 for correct products; 1 for correct underlining]**
(d) $AgNO_3(aq) + NaCl(aq) \longrightarrow AgCl(s) + NaNO_3(aq)$ **[1 for correct formulae of reactants; 1 for correct formulae of products; 1 for correct state symbols]**

16. (a) 160
(b) 112(g)
(c) 102
(d) 102g of Al_2O_3 contains 54g of aluminium **[1]** so 51g contains 27(g) **[1]**.
(e) (i) **Any three from:** Negative oxide ions **[1]** are attracted because they have opposite charge **[1]**. They lose electrons **[1]** to form oxygen atoms / molecules **[1]**. $2O^{2-} \longrightarrow O_2 + 4e^-$ **[1 for correct half equation]**
(ii) **Any three from:** Positive aluminium ions **[1]** are attracted because they have opposite charge **[1]**. They gain electrons **[1]** to form aluminium atoms **[1]**. $Al^{3+} + 3e^- \longrightarrow Al$ **[1 for correct half equation]**

17. (a) (i) **Any one from:** Magnesium ion; Positive ion **[No marks for 'Magnesium' or 'Magnesium atom'.]**
(ii) Delocalised electron
(b) Electrostatic force
(c) The delocalised electrons **[1]** are able to move **[1]** and so carry the charge.
(d) External forces cause the layers of metal ions to move by sliding over each other **[1]**. When the metal ions are displaced, they are held in their new positions by strong forces of attraction from the delocalised electrons **[1]**.

Module C6: Chemical Synthesis
(Pages 64–77)

1. (a) (i) **Lines should be drawn from** Sulfuric acid **to** Copper sulfate **and from** Copper sulfate **to** Copper oxide.
   Lines should be drawn from Hydrochloric acid **to** Magnesium chloride **and from** Magnesium chloride **to** Magnesium oxide.
   [1 for each correct line.]
(ii) **Harmful**
(iii) **Any one from:** Wear goggles; Wear gloves
(b) **Symbol E should be ticked.**

2. (a) Aluminium sulfate; Water
(b) Limewater **should be ticked**.
(c) Unreacted aluminium oxide
(d) **This is a model answer which would score full marks:**
Lizzy should filter the mixture to remove the insoluble, unreacted aluminium oxide. She should then heat the solution of aluminium sulfate to evaporate some of the water and leave the mixture to cool to allow crystals to form. She should then place the crystals in an oven or desiccator to dry them.

3. (a) less than; greater than; citric; sulfuric; gas
(b) (i) Salt; Hydrogen
(ii) Salt; Water
(iii) Salt; Water
(iv) Salt; Water; Carbon dioxide

(c) (i) H^+
(ii) OH^-
(iii) $H^+ + OH^- \longrightarrow H_2O$

4. (a) **This is a model answer which would score full marks:**
An exothermic reaction releases energy into the surroundings, usually as heat. An endothermic reaction absorbs energy from the surroundings. You can classify a reaction as exothermic or endothermic by recording the temperature change of the surroundings. For example, burning is an exothermic reaction because if you burn a fuel below a beaker of water, the temperature of the water increases.
(b) **Any one from:** The reaction mixture getting too hot; Possibility of an explosion; Melting the equipment

5. risk; temperature; purified; crystallise; desiccator

6. (a) (i) **Any one from:** 12; 13; 14
(ii) The universal indicator in the acid has gone from red to green **[1]**, which indicates that the acid has been neutralised **[1]**.
(b) (i) **Any one from:** Use the same amount of acid; Use acid from the same bottle; Use acid of the same concentration.
   Any one from: Add one tablet to each beaker; Add the same mass of tablet to each beaker.
(ii) Peptocool **[1]** because it has increased the pH more than the other two **[1]**.
(c) Calcium chloride + Carbon dioxide + Water **[All three required for 1 mark.]**
(d) Magnesium + Hydrochloric acid $\longrightarrow$ Magnesium chloride **[1]** + Hydrogen **[1]**
   Magnesium carbonate + Hydrochloric acid $\longrightarrow$ Magnesium chloride + Carbon dioxide **[1]** + Water **[1]**
   Hydrogen is flammable but carbon dioxide is harmless in your stomach **[1]**.
   [The mark for magnesium chloride can be awarded to either but not both word equations.]

7. (a) RFM of $CaCO_3$ = 100
   RFM of CaO = 56
   So 200g of $CaCO_3$ will produce 112(g) of CaO
   [1 for correct working but wrong answer]
(b) (i) Nitric acid
(ii) $\frac{8}{12} \times 100 = 66.7(\%)$
   [1 for correct working but wrong answer]

8. (a) (i) Pipette
(ii) Conical flask
(iii) Burette
(b) conical flask; burette; drop; neutralised; distilled
(c) $\frac{20 \times 0.15}{25} = 0.12(mol/dm^3)$
   [1 for correct working but wrong answer]

9. (a) **Any one from:** The amount of product made per unit time; The amount of reactant used per unit time.
   ['The speed at which a reaction occurs' would also gain 1 mark.]
(b) **Any two from:** To maximise the amount of product made in a certain time; To make product more quickly; To slow down unwanted reactions
(c) Smelling the reaction mixture **should be ticked**.

10. (a) Increase the concentration; Increase the temperature; Grind lumps of the reactant into a powder / Increase the surface area of the reactant; Add a catalyst
   ['Increase pressure' would also be acceptable.]
(b) They are used up in the reaction: false; They are always solids: false; They are chemically unchanged at the end of the reaction: true; They reduce the amount of energy needed by the reactants: true
(c) collision; energy; activation
(d) **This is a model answer which would score full marks:**
Increasing the concentration of an aqueous solution will

speed up a chemical reaction because reactant particles will be more crowded, so collisions will be more frequent. Grinding lumps of a solid reactant into a powder will increase its surface area, exposing more reactant particles and so, again, collisions will be more frequent.

11. (a)

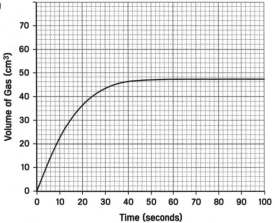

[1 for plotting points correctly; 1 for a smooth curve of best fit.]

(b) 50 (seconds)

(c) 47 (cm³)

(d) **Any suitable answer, e.g.**

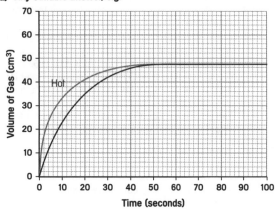

[1 for the line being steeper at start; 1 for the line finishing at same height]

(e) **Any suitable answer, e.g.**

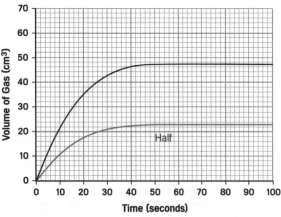

[1 for the line finishing at half the height of the original line.]

12. (a) **Any two from:** There would be a fast / violent / dangerous reaction; The potassium would float; The potassium would fizz; There would be bubbles of gas / hydrogen produced; The potassium / hydrogen would catch fire.

(b) (i) $2KOH + H_2SO_4 \longrightarrow K_2SO_4 + 2H_2O$

(ii) **Lines should be drawn from** H^+ **to** Sulfuric acid **and from** Sulfuric acid **to** SO_4^{2-}.
Lines should be drawn from K^+ **to** Potassium hydroxide **and from** Potassium hydroxide **to** OH^-.
[1 for each correct line.]

(iii) The reaction is a neutralisation reaction: true; You can tell when the reaction has finished because it will stop fizzing: false; The ionic equation for this reaction is $H^+ + OH^- \longrightarrow H_2O$: true; All acids contain OH^- ions: false

13. **Any suitable answer, e.g.**

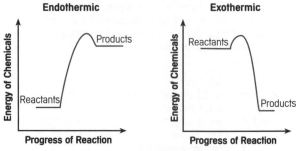

[1 for endothermic graph finishing higher than it starts and for exothermic graph finishing lower than it starts; 1 for correct placement of reactants and products labels on both graphs; 1 for both graphs rising before they fall.]

14. (a) $Fe_2O_3 + 2Al \longrightarrow 2Fe + Al_2O_3$ **[1 for correct formulae; 1 for balancing correctly]**

(b) (i) 160
(ii) 102

(c) 160g of Fe_2O_3 would require $2 \times 27g$ of Al = 54g of Al
So 16g of Fe_2O_3 would require 5.4(g) of Al
[1 for correct working but wrong answer]

(d) 160g of Fe_2O_3 should produce $2 \times 56g$ of Fe = 112g of Fe
So 16g of Fe_2O_3 should produce 11.2(g) of Fe
[1 for correct working but wrong answer]

15. (a) **Any one from:** The carbon dioxide has escaped; She cannot measure the mass of the carbon dioxide.

(b) 123.5

(c) 0.44(g)

(d) $(0.40 \div 0.57) \times 100 = 70(\%)$
[1 for correct working but wrong answer]

Module P4: Explaining Motion (Pages 78–89)

1. (a) (i) Samantha ran 150m in 20 seconds **should be ticked**.
(ii) Speed = Distance ÷ Time = $1200 \div 150 = 8(m/s)$
[1 for correct working but wrong answer]
(iii) The runner is unlikely to run at exactly the same speed for the whole race.
(iv) The speed (of an object) at a particular time

(b) Velocity includes direction.

(c) **Any one from:** Acceleration is the rate at which the velocity of an object changes; Acceleration is a measure of how quickly an object speeds up or slows down.

2. gradient; speed; faster **and** horizontal **should be ringed.**

3. (a) False
(b) True
(c) True
(d) False

4. (a)

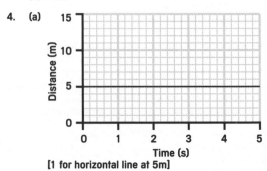

[1 for horizontal line at 5m]

(b)

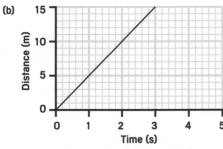

[1 for sloping line with a gradient of 5]

5. **(a)** gradient; acceleration; quickly **and** horizontal **should be ringed**.
   (b) **(i)** Point A marked at (0, 0)
      (ii) Point B marked anywhere on line between (3, 15) and (5, 15)
      (iii) Point C marked anywhere on line between (0, 0) and (3, 15)

6. **(a)** **Any one from:** Change in velocity and Time taken for change; Force and Mass
   (b) metres per second^2 (m/s^2) **should be ticked**.
   (c) **(i)** Acceleration = Change in velocity ÷ Time
         = 15 ÷ 5 = 3m/s^2
         [1 for correct working but wrong answer]
      (ii) Acceleration = Change in velocity ÷ Time
         = 14 ÷ 4 = 3.5m/s^2
         [1 for correct working but wrong answer]
      (iii) Deceleration = Change in velocity ÷ Time
         = 40 ÷ 2 = 20m/s^2
         [1 for correct working but wrong answer]

7. **(a)**

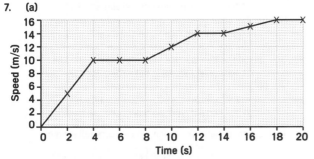

[1 for correctly labelling the x-axis, including units; 1 for correctly labelling the y-axis, including units; 1 for correctly plotting the points]
   (b) **(i)** Acceleration = 10 ÷ 4 = 2.5(m/s^2)
         [1 for correct working but wrong answer]
      (ii) Acceleration = 4 ÷ 4 = 1(m/s^2)
         [1 for correct working but wrong answer]
   (c) Average speed = Total distance ÷ Total time
      = 228 ÷ 20 = 11.4(m/s)
      [1 for correct working but wrong answer]

8. **(a)**

Name of Force	Description of Force
Friction	Acts to slow things down when two surfaces rub against each other
Air resistance	**Friction caused by objects moving through air**
Reaction of the surface	Pushes up on the bottom of a cup sitting on a table and stops the cup sinking into the table
Gravity	**Any one from: Attracts two masses towards each other; Attracts a mass towards the centre of the Earth**

   (b) **This is a model answer which would score full marks:**
   A jet engine pushes gas backwards (action), forcing the jet forwards (reaction). Initially the forwards force is greater than the air resistance, so the jet accelerates. As the speed increases, so does the air resistance until the air resistance balances the forwards force. When the forces are balanced the jet will continue forward at a steady speed until a braking force is applied to slow it down.

(c) Any two suitable examples with suitable explanation, e.g. The brakes of a car [1] use friction between the wheels and the pads to slow down the car [1]; When climbing a wall [1], friction between hands and feet and the wall provides grip [1].

9. **(a)** The size of the force **and** The direction of the force **should be ticked.**
   (b) The combined effect of all the forces acting on an object [1], resulting from adding the forces together [1].
   (c) **(i)** → 3000N [1]; The car will accelerate / speed up [1].
      (ii) ← 2000N [1]; The car will decelerate / slow down [1].
      (iii) ON [1]; The car will continue at the same velocity [1].
   (d) **(i)** 2N [1] to the right [1]
      (ii) 3N [1] up [1]
   (e) **(i)** Noah
      (ii) Anna
      (iii) Bob

10. **(a)**

B	A	D	C

   [1 for each correctly placed up to a maximum of 3.]
   (b) **This is a model answer which would score full marks:**
   As Caitlin exits the plane, the only force acting on her is gravity, so she accelerates downwards. As her speed increases, so does the air resistance, so her acceleration decreases. When the air resistance, equals the force of gravity, the forces are balanced and she falls at a constant speed. When Caitlin's parachute opens, air resistance increases and is then greater than the force of gravity, so she decelerates. As her speed reduces, so does the air resistance until the two forces become balanced. She then falls at a lower constant speed than previously until she hits the ground and becomes stationary.

11. **(a)** A lorry travelling at 50mph **should be ticked**.
    (b) not change; mass; velocity **['mass' and 'velocity' in any order]**

12.

Momentum (kg m/s)	Mass (kg)	Velocity (m/s)
500	50	10
30 000	1000	30
3000	**100**	30
800	400	**2**

13. **This is a model answer which would score full marks:**
The crumple zone of a car is designed to increase the time of the collision. This reduces the momentum over a longer period of time, which reduces the acceleration. As a result the force exerted on the people in the car is reduced. This results in fewer injuries.

14. **(a)** Use the tape measure to measure a set distance [1] and the stopwatch to measure the time taken to travel this distance, so that its velocity can be calculated [1]. Use the electronic balance to measure the mass of the trolley [1].
    (b) **(i)** At 2m/s, 1J [1]; At 4m/s, 4J [1]
       (ii) As the velocity increases, the kinetic energy increases [1]. As the velocity doubles, the kinetic energy more than doubles [1].
       (iii) **The graph should be extended to pass through the origin [1]**. At zero velocity, there is no kinetic energy [1].

15. **(a)** **(i)** A pendulum at the top of its swing **should be ticked**.
       (ii) A cyclist at the top of a hill **should be ticked**.
    (b) gravitational; kinetic
    (c) Gravitational potential energy
       = Weight × Vertical height difference
       = 500 × 100 = 50 000J
       [1 for correct working; 1 for correct answer; 1 for correct units]

16. Work done = Force × Distance moved in the direction of the force
Work done = 10 × 500 = 5000J
[1 for correct working; 1 for correct answer; 1 for correct units]

17. (a) Average velocity = Total displacement ÷ Total time
  = 0 ÷ 12 = 0(m/s)
  [1 for correct working but wrong answer]
(b) Average speed = Total distance ÷ Total time
  = (12 + 12) ÷ 12 = 24 ÷ 12 = 2(m/s)
  [1 for correct working but wrong answer]
(c) Speed = Distance ÷ Time = 12 ÷ 6 = 2(m/s)
  [1 for correct working but wrong answer]
(d) Any one from: The object is not moving at a constant speed; The object is accelerating or decelerating.

18. (a) changing; speeding up; slowing down
(b) Average speed = Total distance ÷ Total time
  = 200 ÷ 25 = 8(m/s)
  [1 for correct working but wrong answer]

19. This is a model answer which would score full marks:
The velocity of the car increases between A and B as the car accelerates from rest. The velocity decreases between B and C and the car comes to rest momentarily before the velocity then increases between C and D but with the car travelling in the opposite direction. The velocity decreases again between D and E until the car comes to rest.

20. (a)
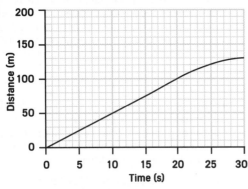

  [1 for straight line from (0, 0) to (20, 100); 1 for curved line from (20, 100) levelling off at (30, 130)]
(b) 110(m)
(c) Kinetic energy = $\frac{1}{2}$ × Mass × Velocity^2
    $560 = \frac{1}{2} \times 70 \times$ Velocity^2
  Velocity^2 = 16
  Velocity = 4m/s
  [1 for correct working; 1 for correct answer; 1 for correct units]

Module P5: Electric Circuits
(Pages 90–101)

1. current; voltage; proportional; voltage; doubled

2. (a) The rod has lost electrons **should be ticked**.
(b) There are free electrons in the wire to allow a current to flow; A current will flow in the wire **and** Some energy in the wire will be lost as heat on discharge **should be ticked**.
(c) The two rods will repel.

3. (a) (i) $V_1 = V_2 + V_3$
    $20 = V_2 + 8$
    $V_2 = 12$ (volts)
    [1 for correct working but wrong answer]
(ii) V = IR
    $12 = 2 \times R$
    $R = 6(\Omega)$
    [1 for correct working but wrong answer]
(b) (i) $V_2 = 20 - 4 = 16(V)$
    V = IR
    $16 = I \times 16$
    $I = 1$ (amp)
    [1 for correct working but wrong answer]

(ii) Work done = Voltage × Units of charge moved
    = 16 × 3 = 48 (joules)
    [1 for correct working but wrong answer]
(c) This is a model answer which would score full marks:
The resistance of the thermistor rises as it cools in the ice. The value shown by V_3 would increase and the value shown on V_2 would decrease. The value of the current in the circuit would decrease as the total resistance increases.

4. charge; amps; conductors; not used

5. Wires contain electrons **[1]**. The battery pushes these electrons around the complete circuit **[1]**. Energy is carried from the battery and lost as heat in the resistor **[1]**. Collisions occur between the moving electrons and vibrating ions, generating heat in the resistor **[1]**.

6. (a) Jason
(b) Toni

7. (a) There will be no force on the wire **should be ticked**.
(b) Any two from: Move the magnet away from the coil; Reverse the magnet and move it towards the coil; Rotate the coil through 180° and move the magnet towards it.
(c) A and C **should be ticked**.

8. (a) (i) Current = Power rating in watts ÷ Voltage
    = (1.84 × 1000) ÷ 230 = 8(A)
    [1 for correct working but wrong answer]
(ii) Voltage = Current × Resistance
    so Resistance = Voltage ÷ Current
    Resistance = 230 ÷ 8 = 28.75(Ω)
    [1 for correct working but wrong answer]
(b) (i) For each lamp Voltage = Current × Resistance
    so Current = Voltage ÷ Resistance
    Current = 230 ÷ 460 = 0.5(A)
    So the total current from the mains = 3 × 0.5 = 1.5(A)
    [1 for correct working but wrong answer]
(ii) Current = Voltage ÷ Resistance
    = 230 ÷ (460 + 460 + 460) = 0.17(A)
    [1 for correct working but wrong answer]

9. This is a model answer which would score full marks:

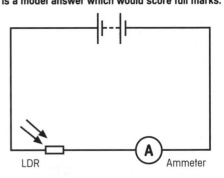

 Torch

Lam should place the torch bulb a short distance from the light dependent resistor (LDR) and measure the distance with a ruler. He should then measure the current reading on the ammeter and record both in a table. He should repeat this process for at least six different distances, which should be repeated and averaged. Lam could then plot a graph of current against distance to show the relationship.

10. (a) (i)

Distance of the Torch from the Component (cm)	Voltage (V)	Current (A)	Resistance (Ω)
20	6	0.6	10
40	6	0.5	12
60	6	**0.4**	15
80	6	0.3	**20**
100	6	0.2	30

    (ii) Light dependent resistor (LDR)

(b) Yes **[1]**. As the distance increases from 20cm to 40cm, the current reduces by 0.1A. However, when it increases from 40cm to 80cm the current reduces by 0.2A **[1]**.

(c) Toni **[1]** because with more readings over a larger range it will become clear if there is a trend. This will give more support to her conclusion **[1]**.

11. A_1: 0.4(A);
A_3: 0.4(A);
V_2: 3(V);
V_3: 3(V)

12. (a) (i) The component heats up.
    (ii) The resistance of short wires is very small when compared to the resistance of components in the circuit (so it can be ignored in calculations).

(b) The greater the voltage across a component, the greater the current flowing through it **and** Two insulators with similar charges will repel each other **should be ticked**.

(c) A direct current from a battery is a current that flows in the same direction all the time, whereas the alternating current from the mains is a current that reverses direction many times a second.

13. A transformer can change the size of a direct current (d.c.) **should be ticked**.

14. (a) Increase the voltage of the battery (or the current from it); Use more turns of wire on the coil; Use a stronger magnet in the motor.

(b) A commutator ensures that the direction of the current is reversed **[1]** at an appropriate point in each revolution **[1]**.

15.

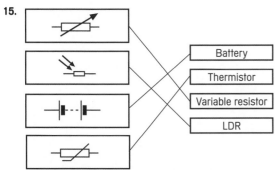

[1 for each correct line up to a maximum of 3.]

16. (a) As the magnet rotates, magnetic field lines cut the wire, generating a voltage (potential difference) across the coil.

(b) This is a model answer which would score full marks:
As the magnet rotates, the direction of the voltage (potential difference) changes every half turn of the magnet. The value of the voltage also changes every half turn and is at a maximum when the poles of the magnet are parallel to the coil with the most field lines cutting the wire in the coil.

17. C and D **should be ticked**.

18. A change in the resistance of one component in the circuit will not affect the potential differences across the other components **should be ticked**.

19. (a) Units used = 768 ÷ 8 = 96(kWh)
[1 for correct working but wrong answer]

(b) Units used in kWh = Power rating in kW × Time in hours
So Power rating = Units used ÷ Time in hours
= 96 ÷ (2 × 24) = 2(kW)
[1 for correct working but wrong answer]

(c) Units used = 40 ÷ 8 = 5
Units used in kWh = Power rating in kW × Time in hours
So Time in hours = Units used ÷ Power rating in kW
= 5 ÷ 0.25 = 20 (hours)
[1 for correct working but wrong answer]

20.

E	C	B	A	D

[1 for each correctly placed up to a maximum of 4.]
[If there is an incorrect answer then C before B gains 1 mark; A before D gains 1 mark. Any two letters in the correct order gains 1 mark.]

21. (a) This is a model answer which would score full marks:
The alternating current flowing due to the 230V alternating voltage induces a changing magnetic field in the primary coil. This flows backwards and forwards around the soft iron core as iron is easily magnetised and demagnetised. The changing magnetic field in the soft iron core passes through the secondary coil, inducing an alternating voltage (potential difference) across it. As the ratio of turns in the primary coil to the secondary coil is 100:1, the voltage is stepped down to 2.3V.

(b) $\dfrac{\text{Primary voltage}}{\text{Secondary voltage}} = \dfrac{\text{No. of turns on the primary coil}}{\text{No. of turns on secondary coil}}$
Primary voltage = (40 ÷ 320) × 160 = 20(V)
[1 for correct working but wrong answer]

Module P6: Radioactive Materials (Pages 102–112)

1. C and E **should be ticked**.

2. Lines should be drawn from Alpha **to** Stopped by paper; **from** Beta **to** Stopped by 4mm of aluminium but not by paper; **and from** Gamma **to** Only stopped by several centimetres of lead.
[1 for each correct line up to a maximum of 2.]

3. A microwave oven **should be ticked**.

4. (a) (i) Peer review. Nine different countries and 7000 individual cases were used to produce the study.
    (ii) Radon gas emits short-range alpha particles which cannot penetrate the outside layer of the skin **[1]**. Only when it enters the lungs can it cause serious damage to body cells **[1]**.

(b) This is a model answer which would score full marks:
The report does not look at other possible causes, for example smoking or genetics (history of lung cancer in the family). In addition, the study does not look at variables such as age, sex or ethnic group. People can live in areas of high exposure to radon gas but still develop lung cancer for other reasons. Not all people exposed to radon gas develop lung cancer. The report does not mention if a control group was studied, possibly similar people in areas with very low radon gas emissions, to see if the reported cases of lung cancer were clearly lower.

5. There are only protons and neutrons in the nucleus of an atom **should be ticked**.

6. (a) (i) Gamma
    (ii) Beta
    (iii) Alpha
    (iv) Gamma

(b) (i) This is a model answer which would score full marks:
The teacher must use forceps to handle the sources and keep both himself and the students at a sensible distance from the sources at all times, to avoid too much irradiation. For each source in turn, place the paper in front of it and use the Geiger counter to measure the

radiation passing through in a certain time. The Geiger counter should be only a few centimetres from the source and the counts for each source should be recorded. The time, measured with the stopwatch, and the distance of the source from the Geiger counter should be kept the same for all the measurements of radiation. Repeat the process for the sheet of aluminium and the piece of lead.

    (ii) Gamma radiation

    (iii) The background count (to subtract from his experimental readings)

(c) **(i)** Ionising radiation can damage living cells / cause cancer / cause mutations **[1]** but background radiation is at a safe level **[1]**.

    (ii) Sievert

    (iii) Exposure to ionising radiation

7. **(a)** **(i)** The radiologist

    (ii) The patient

    (iii) Irradiation

(b) The patient will be emitting beta particles due to the radioiodine and these can travel a short distance in the air **[1]**. By keeping a reasonable distance, the relatives will be out of range of the beta particles **[1]**.

8. **(a)** Gamma

(b) **This is a model answer which would score full marks:**
A source with a half-life of a few days should be chosen so that the radiation can fall to a safe level in a time long enough to destroy the tumour but not so long that it causes major damage to living cells. A source with a half-life of a few hours would decay before it could successfully irradiate the tumour, whilst a source with a half-life of a few weeks would be likely to cause damage to living tissue because they would be exposed to high levels of radiation for too long.

9. **(a)** **(i)** Y

    (ii) Z

    (iii) X

(b) The time taken for the activity of a radioactive source to fall to half of its starting value is called the half-life; The further you are from a radioactive source, the less radiation your body is exposed to **and** Lead shields are used in hospitals to protect medical staff from exposure to radiation **should be ticked**.

10. half-life; alpha; beta

11. **(a)** **(i)** Too much exposure could lead to damage to the body cells or radiation sickness.

    (ii) **Any suitable answer, e.g.** A worker in the nuclear industry; Medical staff; Nuclear research scientist

(b) **(i)** A controlled dose of intense ionising radiation can be administered to the affected area for a limited amount of time **[1]** by a tracer or by a beam of gamma rays to kill cancer cells **[1]**.

    (ii) The patient: There is a small risk of damaging cells around the cancer cells.
The medical staff: There is a higher risk of damaging their own body cells / getting cancer due to increased exposure.

(c) **Any two from:** Use a lead shield; Keep as large a distance as possible from the source; Limit the time of exposure to ionising radiation.

12. A and D **should be ticked**.

13. **Any four from:** Radon; Medical; Food; Cosmic rays; Gamma rays from rocks or buildings; Nuclear industry; Nuclear weapons testing / fallout

14. v: 234; w: 2; x: 234; y: −1

15. **(a)** **(i)** 1 minute **should be ticked**.

    (ii) 4 minutes **should be ringed**.

(b) $208 \times \left(\frac{1}{2}\right)^5 = 6.5\,(\text{g})$
[1 for correct working but wrong answer]

(c) The nucleus loses four protons **[1]** and four neutrons **[1]**.

16. **(a)** **This is a model answer which would score full marks:**
A neutron is absorbed by the nucleus and it makes the nucleus unstable causing it to split into two almost equal parts, which become radioactive waste. Three neutrons are released and a large quantity of energy is released, mostly in the form of heat. In a nuclear reactor, one neutron, on average, goes on to further fission reactions with uranium nuclei, leading to large releases of energy and a small amount of radioactive waste material being produced.

(b) Each fission releases energy and further neutrons **[1]** and at least one neutron from each fission goes on to further fission, releasing more energy **[1]**.

(c) Control rods are raised or lowered to absorb fewer or more neutrons **[1]**, so that, on average, just one neutron from each fission goes on to further fission, meaning a constant rate of energy release **[1]**.

17. Isotopes of the same element always have the same number of protons **and** Isotopes of an element always have the same number of protons but a different number of neutrons **should be ticked**.

18. **(a)** **Any suitable answer, e.g.** The ionising radiation used is gamma as it passes through the body and there is only a small risk of damage to body cells **[1]**. It can be detected easily outside the body and used to produce detailed images of internal organs **[1]**. Medical staff will use sources with a short half-life so that they are quickly eliminated from the body **[1]**. They will keep the dosage as low as possible (ALARA principle) and monitor their exposure to radiation using special film badges **[1]**. **['Glass shields containing lead can be used to reduce exposure to gamma radiation' is also acceptable.]**

(b) An isotope of thorium, atomic number 90 **should be ticked**.

19. **(a)** There are two forces that are balanced **[1]**. The repulsive force between the positively charged protons trying to force the nucleus apart is balanced by the strong force which is an attractive, short-ranged force between the particles in the nucleus, and this holds it together **[1]**.

(b) **(i)** $E = mc^2 = (3.1 \times 10^{-28}) \times (9 \times 10^{16})$
         $= 2.79 \times 10^{-11}\,(\text{J})$
[1 for correct working but wrong answer]

    (ii) No. of nuclei = $1.0\,\text{J} \div (2.79 \times 10^{-11}\,\text{J})$
         $= 3.58 \times 10^{10}$
[1 for correct working but wrong answer]

11. For each use of a metal, draw a line to the relevant property and another line from the property to the explanation of that property. One line has been drawn for you. [5]

Use	Property	Explanation
Copper used for electrical wiring	Malleable and strong	Close-packed metal ions transfer vibrations effectively
Aluminium used for saucepans	Good conductor of heat	Strong bonds between metal ions can re-form in a new shape
Steel used for car body panels	Good electrical conductor	Strong bonds between metal ions take a lot of energy to overcome
Titanium used for heat exchangers	High melting point	Delocalised electrons are free to move

12. **(a)** Draw lines to show the impact on the environment of each method of disposal. [2]

Method	Impact on environment
Reusing metals	Uses a lot less energy than mining the ore and extracting the metal
Recycling metals	Landfill sites destroy natural habitats and heavy metals can pollute groundwater
Throwing away metals	Very little environmental impact

(b) Give **three** environmental impacts of mining metals and metal ores. [3]

1. ....

2. ....

3. ....

[Total: .... / 98]

13. The dot-cross diagram shows the covalent bonding in water.

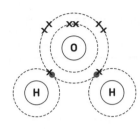

(a) The nuclei of the oxygen atom and both hydrogen atoms are positively charged. Why do they not repel each other and force the molecule apart? [2]

_____

_____

(b) Explain why all three atoms in the molecule of water are stable. [1]

_____

(c) Draw a dot-cross diagram showing the covalent bonding in a molecule of methane (CH_4). [2]

14. You may find that the data sheet on page 114 helps you to answer this question.

Zoe works as a chemist at a water supply company. She tests the water regularly to ensure that it is safe for customers to drink.

(a) Copper ions are harmful to people. Describe the test that Zoe would perform to see if there are copper ions present in the water. Describe what the positive result would be. Use an ionic equation in your answer. [4]

_____

_____

_____

(b) Zoe takes a sample of water and adds hydrochloric acid to it. Nothing happens. She then adds barium chloride to the sample and a white solid forms, which falls to the bottom of the test tube. What **two** conclusions can Zoe make about the ions present in this water sample? [2]

1. ....

2. ....

(c) The following week, Zoe hears that the water might have been contaminated with an iron compound. It is possible that the compound is one of the following:

Iron(II) chloride

Iron(II) bromide

Iron(II) iodide

Iron(III) chloride

Iron(III) bromide

Iron(III) iodide

Describe and justify two tests that Zoe should perform and how her results will confirm the compound present in the water.

🖉 *The quality of written communication will be assessed in your answer to this question.* [6]

....

....

....

....

....

....

....

....

15. The tables below give information about the solubility of some substances. Use the data in the tables for this question.

Soluble in Water	
Sodium chloride	Sodium carbonate
Sodium nitrate	Calcium nitrate
Calcium chloride	Silver nitrate

Insoluble in Water
Calcium carbonate
Silver carbonate
Silver chloride

(a) When sodium carbonate solution is mixed with calcium chloride solution, a precipitate is formed. What is it? [1]

_____

(b) Which two solutions could be mixed to form an insoluble precipitate containing silver ions? [2]

_____

(c) What would you expect to see if calcium nitrate solution was mixed with sodium carbonate? Write a word equation and underline any precipitate that you would expect to see.

(i) Observation: _____ [1]

(ii) Word equation: _____ [2]

(d) Write a symbol equation, including state symbols, for the reaction between silver nitrate (AgNO$_3$) and sodium chloride solutions. [3]

_____

16. (a) Work out the relative formula mass of Fe$_2$O$_3$. [1]

_____

(b) What mass of iron could be extracted from 160g of Fe$_2$O$_3$? [1]

_____ g

(c) Work out the relative formula mass of Al$_2$O$_3$. [1]

_____

(d) What mass of aluminium could be extracted from 51g of Al$_2$O$_3$? [2]

_____ g

(e) During the electrolysis of aluminium oxide, Al^{3+} ions and oxide ions (O^{2-}) are free to move in the electrolyte. State and explain which ions are attracted to each electrode and what happens to them, using ideas about electrons. Use half equations in your answer.

(i) Positive electrode (anode): .... [4]

....

....

(ii) Negative electrode (cathode): .... [4]

....

....

17. The diagram shows metallic bonding.

(a) Label the two different types of particle in the lattice structure. [2]

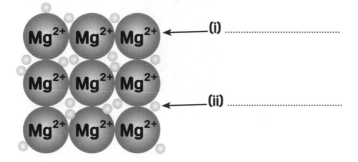

(i) ....

(ii) ....

(b) What type of force holds together the oppositely charged particles in a metal? [1]

....

(c) Explain how metals conduct electricity. [2]

....

....

(d) Explain how the structure and bonding in metals allows them to be malleable. [2]

....

....

[Total: .... / 46]

1. Joe decides he wants to make crystals of different salts to investigate their shapes and colours.

   (a) Two of the salts he wants to make are copper sulfate and magnesium chloride.

   (i) Draw lines to show which two reactants Joe should use to make each of these salts. [4]

Reactant	Product	Reactant
Nitric acid		Copper oxide
	Copper sulfate	
Hydrochloric acid		Magnesium oxide
	Magnesium chloride	
Sulfuric acid		Iron oxide

   (ii) Joe looks at the bottle of hydrochloric acid.

   What does the symbol on the label mean? [1]

   _____

   (iii) Suggest a safety precaution that Joe should observe when using hydrochloric acid. [1]

   _____

   (b) Joe's teacher tells him that the solution of copper sulfate he has made is toxic. Which of the hazard symbol stickers should Joe put on the beaker containing his copper sulfate solution? Put a tick (✓) in the box next to the correct answer. [1]

   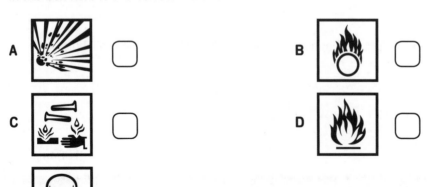

2. Lizzy decides to make some aluminium sulfate crystals. She reacts aluminium oxide with sulfuric acid.

(a) Complete the word equation for this reaction. [2]

Aluminium oxide + Sulfuric acid ⟶ .... + ...

(b) After the reaction, Lizzy tests the pH of the solution to make sure it is neutral. Which of the following would **not** be suitable for this purpose? Put a tick (✓) in the box next to the unsuitable method. [1]

Universal indicator ☐

Limewater ☐

pH probe ☐

(c) Lizzy notices some white solid in the bottom of the beaker which contains the neutral aluminium sulfate solution. Suggest what the insoluble white solid might be. [1]

....

(d) Lizzy wants to remove the unwanted white solid from the solution of aluminium sulfate and then make crystals of aluminium sulfate. Describe how she should do this. Include all the steps in the process and explain why each one is needed.

🖉 *The quality of written communication will be assessed in your answer to this question.* [6]

....

....

....

....

....

....

....

....

....

....

3. **(a)** Complete the following paragraph. Use words from this list. [5]

citric **gas** **greater than** **less than** **solid** **sulfuric**

Acids and alkalis are measured on the pH scale, which is usually shown from pH 1 to 14. Acids

have pH values that are _____ 7, while alkalis have pH values that are

_____ 7. A solution with a pH of 7 is said to be neutral. Soluble metal

hydroxides are always alkalis. Some pure acids are solid, such as _____ acid,

while others are liquid, such as ethanoic, nitric and _____ acids. Hydrogen

chloride is an example of an acid that is a _____ at room temperature.

When an acid and an alkali react together, this is called a neutralisation reaction.

(b) Complete the general word equations below.

(i) Acid + Metal ⟶ _____ + _____ [2]

(ii) Acid + Alkali ⟶ _____ + _____ [2]

(iii) Acid + Metal oxide ⟶ _____ + _____ [2]

(iv) Acid + Metal carbonate ⟶ _____ + _____ + _____ [3]

(c) **(i)** Which ion is always present when an acid dissolves in water? Show the charge on the ion. [1]

_____

(ii) Which ion is present in all alkalis? Show the charge on the ion. [1]

_____

(iii) Write an ionic equation to show how water is made in an acid–alkali neutralisation reaction. [1]

_____

4. **(a)** Explain what is meant by the terms **exothermic** and **endothermic**. Describe how you can classify a reaction as exothermic or endothermic. Use an example of a chemical reaction to illustrate one of these terms.

The quality of written communication will be assessed in your answer to this question. [6]

(b) Give a safety factor that industrial chemists would need to consider if a synthetic pathway for the manufacture of a chemical involved a highly exothermic reaction. [1]

5. Complete the following paragraph. Use words from this list. [5]

cost	crystallise	desiccator	dissolve
purified	refrigerator	risk	temperature

Chemical synthesis means making a chemical. There are several steps to making a chemical. First, research chemists choose a sequence of reactions that will make the product. Second, a

.... assessment is carried out to ensure that appropriate safety precautions are

taken. Chemists then work out the quantity of reactants to use and carry out the reaction in suitable

apparatus at the right conditions, for example, concentration and .... The

product is then separated from the reaction mixture, using a technique such as filtration. The product

must then be .... to make sure that it is not contaminated by unreacted

reactants or unwanted products. One way to do this is to evaporate any unwanted water by heating the

solution and then leaving the product to .... The damp crystals can then be

dried in an oven or ....

6. Emily is investigating antacid tablets. Antacid tablets are taken by people who have acid indigestion. The ingredients listed on the packet include calcium carbonate and magnesium carbonate.

(a) Emily adds a tablet to three different liquids and tests the pH of the solution using universal indicator before and after adding the tablet. She also records her observations. Her results are shown in the table.

Liquid	Colour of Universal Indicator Before Adding Tablet	Colour of Universal Indicator After Adding Tablet	Observations
Water	Green	Green	No evidence of a reaction.
Sodium hydroxide	Dark purple	Dark purple	No evidence of a reaction.
Hydrochloric acid	Red	Green	Fizzing. Tablet appears to dissolve.

(i) Suggest a pH value for the sodium hydroxide solution. [1]

....

(ii) How do Emily's observations prove that these tablets would be effective as a treatment for acid indigestion? [2]

....

....

(b) Melissa also investigated antacid tablets. She compared three different tablets to see which was the best. She added the antacid tablets to separate beakers of dilute hydrochloric acid and measured the pH of the solution that was left after each reaction had finished.

(i) Suggest **two** things that Melissa must do in order to make this a fair test. [2]

1. ....

2. ....

(ii) Here are Melissa's results:

Antacid Brand	pH Before Adding Tablet	pH After Adding Tablet
Acideze	1	4
Peptocool	1	6
Gastrocalm	1	5

Which antacid is the best at neutralising stomach acid? Explain your answer. [2]

....

....

(c) One of the active ingredients in these antacid treatments is calcium carbonate. Complete the word equation for the reaction of calcium carbonate with hydrochloric acid. [1]

Calcium carbonate + Hydrochloric acid ⟶ .... + ... + ...

(d) Another common ingredient in antacid treatments is magnesium carbonate. Josh knows that magnesium metal will react with hydrochloric acid to produce a neutral salt. Why is eating a tablet with magnesium metal in it dangerous, whereas eating a tablet containing magnesium carbonate is much safer? Use **two** word equations in your answer. [5]

....

....

....

....

....

....

7. Use the periodic table on page 113 for this question.

When calcium carbonate is heated, it thermally decomposes to form calcium oxide and carbon dioxide, as shown in the following equation:

Calcium carbonate ⟶ Calcium oxide + Carbon dioxide

$$CaCO_3 \longrightarrow CaO + CO_2$$

The theoretical yield (mass) of calcium oxide that could be produced can be calculated using the following formula, where RFM = relative formula mass:

Theoretical yield of calcium oxide = $\dfrac{\text{Mass of calcium carbonate}}{\text{RFM of calcium carbonate}}$ × RFM of calcium oxide

(a) Use the formula to work out the theoretical yield (mass) of calcium oxide that could be formed when 200g of calcium carbonate ($CaCO_3$) is heated. [2]

....

....

....

.... g

(b) Magnesium nitrate, $Mg(NO_3)_2$, was made by reacting an acid with magnesium oxide.
The theoretical yield was 12g but the actual yield was 8g.

(i) State the acid needed to make the product. [1]

....

(ii) Calculate the percentage yield. [2]

....

....

....

.... %

8. The diagram shows the apparatus used to perform a titration.

(a) Label the diagram. [3]

(i) ....

(ii) ....

(iii) ....

(b) Complete the following method for a titration between an aqueous alkali and an aqueous acid using the words below. [5]

burette   conical flask   drop   distilled   neutralised   squirt

1. Use a volumetric pipette to accurately measure 25cm^3 of alkali and put it into a

    ....

2. Add two drops of indicator and note the colour it goes in the alkali.

3. Carefully fill a .... with your acid solution and make sure that it is at zero.

4. Slowly add the acid to the alkali while you carefully swirl the flask to mix the reactants together.

5. As you notice the colour of the indicator start to change, add the acid one

    .... at a time until the indicator changes colour permanently. The alkali

    has now been .... Record the volume of acid used.

6. If you are using a solid acid, you would first need to dissolve it into a measured volume of

    .... water.

(c) In a titration between sodium hydroxide (NaOH) and hydrochloric acid (HCl), the concentration of the alkali can be calculated using the following formula:

$$\text{Concentration of NaOH (mol/dm}^3) = \frac{\text{Volume of HCl (cm}^3) \times \text{Concentration of HCl (mol/dm}^3)}{\text{Volume of NaOH (cm}^3)}$$

Use this formula to calculate the concentration of NaOH if 25cm^3 of NaOH required 20cm^3 of HCl to neutralise it. The HCl had a concentration of 0.15mol/dm^3. [2]

....

.... mol/dm^3

9.   **(a)** Explain what is meant by the term **rate of reaction**. [1]

....

....

(b) Why is it important for chemists to be able to control the rate of a reaction? [2]

....

....

....

(c) Which of these is **not** a method of measuring the rate of a reaction? Put a tick (✓) in the box next to the **incorrect** method. [1]

Collecting a gas ☐   Smelling the reaction mixture ☐

Weighing the reaction mixture ☐   Observing the formation of a precipitate ☐

10. (a) State **four** ways to speed up a chemical reaction. [4]

1. ....

2. ....

3. ....

4. ....

(b) Put a tick (✓) in the correct box to show whether each statement about catalysts is **true** or **false**. [4]

	true	false
They are used up in the reaction.	☐	☐
They are always solids.	☐	☐
They are chemically unchanged at the end of the reaction.	☐	☐
They reduce the amount of energy needed by the reactants.	☐	☐

(c) Complete the following paragraph. Use words from this list. [3]

activation   **atomic**   **collision**   **energy**   **maximum**

We can explain the way that some factors affect the speed of a reaction using

.... theory. This theory states that for particles to react, they must collide

with enough .... This amount is called the .... energy.

(d) Explain how increasing the concentration of an aqueous reactant and grinding up lumps of a solid reactant increase the reaction rate. Use ideas about particles and collisions in your answer.

✎ *The quality of written communication will be assessed in your answer to this question.* [6]

....

....

....

....

....

....

11. Nick carried out an investigation into the reaction between magnesium and excess hydrochloric acid. He measured the total volume of gas produced by the reaction every ten seconds. His data are in the table below.

Time (s)	Volume of Gas (cm³)
0	0
10	24
20	36
30	43
40	46
50	47
60	47
70	47
80	47
90	47
100	47

(a) Plot a graph to show his results. [2]

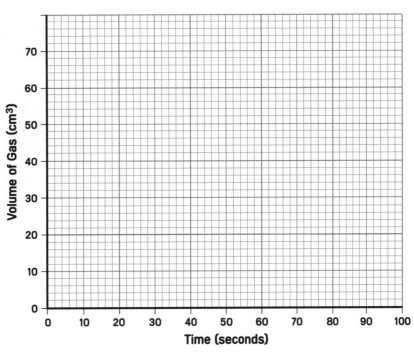

(b) After how many seconds did the reaction stop? [1]

.... seconds

(c) What was the total volume of gas produced? [1]

.... cm³

(d) On the graph, sketch another line to show the results you would expect to see if Nick repeated his experiment with the same volume and concentration of acid and the same amount of magnesium, but this time at a higher temperature. Label your line **Hot**. [2]

(e) On the graph, sketch another line to show the results you would expect if Nick repeated his experiment at the same temperature but with half as much magnesium. Label your line **Half**. [1]

[Total: .... / 102]

12. Ryan wants to make some potassium sulfate, which is a salt used in some fertilisers.

Ryan knows that he can make a salt by reacting a metal with an acid.

Ryan
The simplest way to make potassium sulfate is to react potassium with sulfuric acid.

Jack
Reacting potassium with sulfuric acid would be dangerous because there is a lot of water in sulfuric acid.

(a) Use your knowledge of the reaction with water of elements in Group 1 of the periodic table to predict what Ryan would **see** if he added potassium to a dilute solution of sulfuric acid. [2]

....

....

(b) Ryan follows Jack's advice and uses a different method to make the potassium sulfate, starting with potassium hydroxide.

(i) Balance the symbol equation for the reaction. [1]

.... KOH + ... H_2SO_4 ⟶ .... K_2SO_4 + ... H_2O

(ii) Draw straight lines to show the positive and negative ions present in potassium hydroxide and sulfuric acid. [4]

Positive ions	Reactants	Negative ions
H⁺		Cl⁻
P⁺	Potassium hydroxide	OH⁻
H²⁺		O²⁻
K⁺	Sulfuric acid	S²⁻
K²⁺		SO₄²⁻

(iii) Ryan asks his friends to help him understand the reaction. Below are some of his friends' comments. Put a tick (✓) in the correct box to show whether each statement is **true** or **false**. [4]

	true	false
The reaction is a neutralisation reaction.	⬭	⬭
You can tell when the reaction has finished because it will stop fizzing.	⬭	⬭
The ionic equation for this reaction is $H^+ + OH^- \longrightarrow H_2O$.	⬭	⬭
All acids contain OH^- ions.	⬭	⬭

13. Energy changes in reactions can be represented by energy-level diagrams. Draw energy-level diagrams to show an endothermic reaction and an exothermic reaction. Label your diagrams with the words **reactants** and **products**. [3]

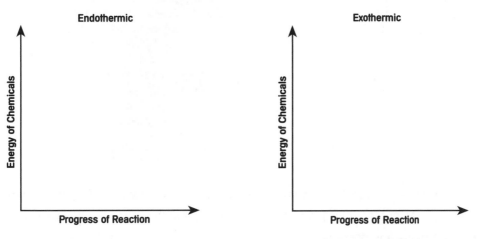

14. Emily is planning to do the thermite reaction, which involves displacing iron from iron oxide (Fe_2O_3) using aluminium powder. The other product of the reaction is aluminium oxide (Al_2O_3).

(a) Represent this reaction as a balanced symbol equation. [2]

....

(b) Calculate the relative formula masses (RFMs) of Fe_2O_3 and Al_2O_3.

   (i) Fe_2O_3: .... [1]

   (ii) Al_2O_3: .... [1]

(c) If Emily starts with 16g of Fe_2O_3, what mass of aluminium should she weigh out for the reaction? [2]

....

....

.... g

(d) What is the theoretical yield of iron in Emily's reaction? [2]

....

....

.... g

15. Simone is investigating the thermal decomposition of copper carbonate. When she heats the solid in a boiling tube, it breaks down forming copper oxide and releasing carbon dioxide.

$$CuCO_3(s) \longrightarrow CuO(s) + CO_2(g)$$

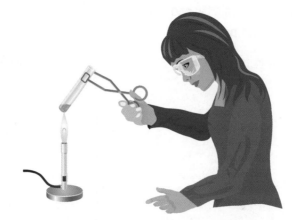

(a) Simone measures the mass of the boiling tube and the powder before the experiment and after she has heated it for ten minutes. She finds that the mass has decreased. Suggest why the mass has decreased. [1]

....

(b) Simone wants to work out the theoretical yield of carbon dioxide, so she calculates the relative formula mass of each compound using relative atomic masses from the periodic table.

Element	Relative Atomic Mass
Copper	63.5
Carbon	12
Oxygen	16

Simone writes her calculated values for the relative formula masses underneath the formulae in the symbol equation. Write the missing value in the space provided. [1]

$$CuCO_3 \longrightarrow CuO + CO_2$$

....   79.5   44

(c) Simone also investigates nickel carbonate, $NiCO_3$, which reacts in a similar way. The relative formula mass of each compound has been written underneath each formula in the balanced symbol equation below.

$$NiCO_3 \longrightarrow NiO + CO_2$$

119   75   44

Simone weighs out 1.19g of nickel carbonate into a boiling tube. What is the theoretical yield of carbon dioxide? [1]

....

.... g

(d) Simone then investigates manganese carbonate. She calculates that by heating 1.5g of manganese carbonate she should produce 0.57g of carbon dioxide. After the experiment, she calculates that 0.40g of carbon dioxide was released. Calculate the percentage yield of her experiment. [2]

....

....

....

.... %

[Total: .... / 27]

P4 Explaining Motion

1. **(a) (i)** Jenny, Amelia, Samantha and Ann have a race to see who can run the fastest. Which sprinter has the greatest average speed? Put a tick (✓) in the box next to the correct answer. [1]

Jenny ran 100m in 15 seconds. ☐   Amelia ran 80m in 12 seconds. ☐

Samantha ran 150m in 20 seconds. ☐   Ann ran 60m in 17 seconds. ☐

(ii) Calculate the average speed of a runner who runs a 1200m race in 150 seconds. [2]

....

.... m/s

(iii) Why is the speed calculated called the average speed? [1]

....

(iv) What does the term **instantaneous speed** mean? [1]

....

(b) How is the **velocity** of an object different from its speed? [1]

....

(c) What does the term **acceleration** mean? [1]

....

2. Put a ring around the correct options in the following sentences. [4]

The **height / gradient** of a distance–time graph is a measure of the **speed / acceleration** of the object.

The steeper the slope, the **faster / slower** the object is moving. The motion of a stationary object is

represented by a **horizontal / vertical** line.

3. The graph shows the motion of three objects.

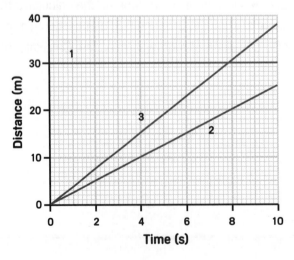

Put a tick (✓) in the correct box to show whether each statement is **true** or **false**. [4]

	true	false
(a) Object 2 is moving more quickly than object 3.	☐	☐
(b) Object 3 is moving at a greater speed than object 1.	☐	☐
(c) Object 1 is stationary.	☐	☐
(d) Objects 2 and 3 are both accelerating.	☐	☐

4. Plot distance–time graphs to represent the following:

(a) Colin standing stationary 5m from a starting point (0). [1]

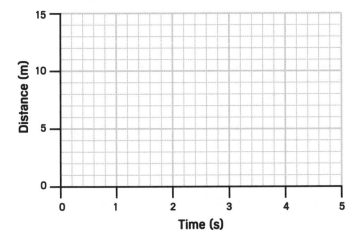

(b) Alice running at a constant speed of 5m/s. [1]

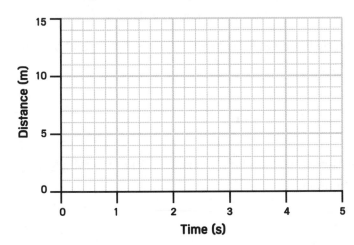

5. **(a)** Put a ring around the correct options in the following sentences. [4]

The **height / gradient** of a speed–time graph is the **speed / acceleration** of the object. The steeper

the slope, the more **quickly / slowly** the object is accelerating. The motion of an object moving

with constant speed is represented by a **horizontal / vertical** line.

(b) On the grid provided, mark the following points. [3]

    (i) Point **A** where the object is stationary

    (ii) Point **B** where the object is moving at a constant speed

    (iii) Point **C** where the object is accelerating

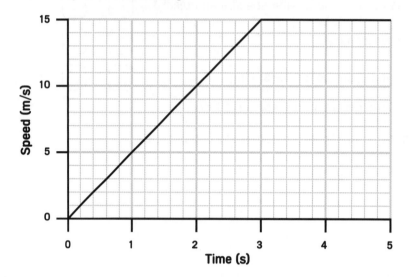

6. **(a)** What **two** things do you need to know to work out the acceleration of an object? [1]

.... and ....

(b) What units are used to measure acceleration? Put a tick (✓) in the box next to the correct answer. [1]

Metres per second (m/s) ☐   Metres per second² (m/s²) ☐

Miles per hour (mph) ☐   Kilometres per hour (km/h) ☐

(c) **(i)** Jane accelerates her car uniformly from rest to a speed of 15m/s in a time of 5 seconds. Calculate the acceleration of the car. [2]

....

....

(ii) Harry is a train driver. He accelerates his train from a speed of 20m/s to 34m/s in 4 seconds. Calculate the acceleration of the train. [2]

....

....

(iii) Matt is a fighter pilot. After travelling at a speed of 40m/s, he lands on an aircraft carrier where he stops. The descent takes 2 seconds. Calculate the deceleration of the plane. [2]

....

....

7. The table shows the speed and time of a motorcyclist for the first 20 seconds of her journey.

Time (s)	0	2	4	6	8	10	12	14	16	18	20
Speed (m/s)	0	5	10	10	10	12	14	14	15	16	16

(a) Label the axes below and plot a speed–time graph of the motorcyclist's journey on the grid below. [3]

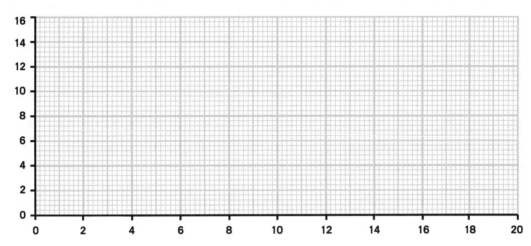

(b) Calculate the following:

(i) The acceleration of the bike in the first 4 seconds. [2]

....

.... m/s²

(ii) The acceleration of the bike after 8 seconds until it reaches a speed of 14m/s. [2]

....

.... m/s²

(c) The total distance travelled was 228m. Calculate the average speed for the whole journey. [2]

....

.... m/s

8. **(a)** Complete the table with the names and descriptions of four forces. [4]

Name of Force	Description of Force
	Acts to slow things down when two surfaces rub against each other
Air resistance	
	Pushes up on the bottom of a cup sitting on a table and stops the cup sinking into the table
Gravity	

(b) Whenever something exerts a force, it experiences an equal and opposite force. Explain how this principle is used in jet engines.

✎ *The quality of written communication will be assessed in your answer to this question.* [6]

_____

_____

_____

_____

_____

_____

_____

_____

_____

_____

(c) Give **two** examples of how friction can be useful and explain how each one works. [4]

1. _____

_____

2. _____

_____

9. **(a)** What **two** things are represented by an arrow on a force diagram? Put ticks (✓) in the boxes next to the **two** correct statements. [2]

The size of the force ☐   The name of the force ☐

The type of force ☐   The direction of the force ☐

(b) What is meant by the term **resultant force**? [2]

....

....

(c) The following diagrams show a car travelling at 30km/h. Calculate the resultant force and state how it affects the car's motion, if at all.

(i)   1000N ←  → 4000N

.... [2]

(ii) 2000N ← 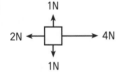 → 0N

.... [2]

(iii)   1000N ← 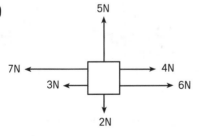 → 1000N

.... [2]

(d) Calculate the size of the resultant force in each case, stating the direction.

(i)

```
        1N
        ↑
2N ←  ☐  → 4N
        ↓
        1N
```

.... [2]

(ii)

```
              5N
              ↑
7N ←       ┌────┐  → 4N
   3N ←    │    │  → 6N
           └────┘
              ↓
              2N
```

.... [2]

(e) A car travelling at 40km/h in a 20km/h zone hits a pedestrian and injures him. Three bystanders make the following observations.

Noah
If the car had been travelling at the speed limit, there may not have been an accident.

Anna
The fact that the driver was speeding means that the pedestrian had no chance of avoiding the accident.

Bob
There are too many uncontrolled factors to come to a conclusion.

(i) Who is suggesting that there is a correlation between speeding and the chance of having an accident? [1]

_____

(ii) Who is suggesting the speeding car caused the accident? [1]

_____

(iii) Who is suggesting a fair test? [1]

_____

10. Caitlin jumps out of a plane. She does not initially open her parachute but freefalls towards the ground. As she falls, she accelerates.

(a) Look at the diagrams of Caitlin as she falls. They are not in the correct order. Put the letters in the empty boxes to show the correct order. [3]

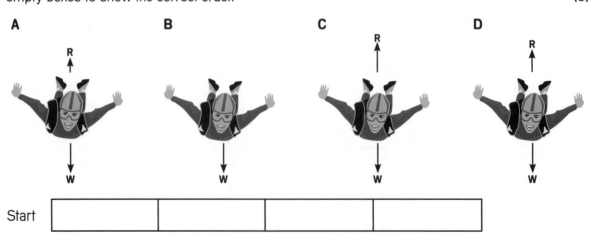

(b) The speed–time graph shows how Caitlin's speed changes after she jumps out of the plane.

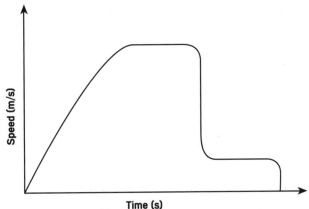

Explain the shape of the graph by describing how the forces acting on Caitlin change as she falls.

✎ *The quality of written communication will be assessed in your answer to this question.* [6]

....

....

....

....

....

....

....

....

....

....

....

11. **(a)** Which object has the greatest momentum? Put a tick (✓) in the box next to the correct answer. [1]

A lorry travelling at 50mph ☐   A car travelling at 50mph ☐

(b) Complete the following sentences. Use words from this list. [3]

change   **not change**   **acceleration**   **mass**

velocity   **stationary**

If the resultant force acting on an object is zero, its momentum will ....

An object's momentum can be increased by increasing its .... or by

increasing its ....

12. Complete the following table. [4]

Momentum (kg m/s)	Mass (kg)	Velocity (m/s)
	50	10
	1000	30
3000		30
800	400	

13. Explain how a crumple zone is used in cars as a safety feature.

The quality of written communication will be assessed in your answer to this question. [6]

_____

_____

_____

_____

_____

_____

14. A student investigates how kinetic energy depends on speed. He has a tape measure, a stopwatch, an electronic balance and a small trolley.

(a) Describe what measurements he needs to make to calculate the trolley's kinetic energy. [3]

_____

_____

(b) This graph shows the results:

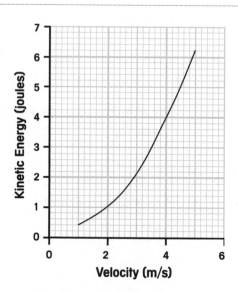

(i) Use the graph to find the kinetic energy at a velocity of 2m/s and 4m/s. [2]

(ii) Describe the trend shown by the graph. [2]

(iii) Extend the graph to show how kinetic energy changes as the velocity reduces to zero and explain why. [2]

15. **(a)** Which object will have more gravitational potential energy? Put a tick (✓) in the box next to the correct answer in each part. [2]

(i) A pendulum at the top of its swing ☐   A pendulum at the bottom of its swing ☐

(ii) A cyclist at the bottom of a hill ☐   A cyclist at the top of a hill ☐

(b) Complete the following sentences. Use words from this list. [2]

chemical   **electrical**   **gravitational**   **kinetic**

As a sledge is pulled up a hill it gains .... potential energy. As it starts to slide

down the hill the energy is turned into .... energy.

(c) Calculate the gain in gravitational potential energy of a climber with a weight of 500N who climbs up a cliff 100m high. Include the units in your answer. [3]

16. Gill pushes her bike home from school a distance of 500m. It takes a force of 10N to overcome the forces of friction. Calculate the amount of work she will have done to get her bike home. Include the units in your answer. [3]

[Total: .... **/ 114]**

17. The displacement–time graph shows the journey of a ball being kicked against a wall.

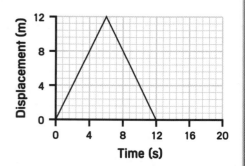

(a) What is the average velocity of this journey? [2]

_____

_____ m/s

(b) What is the average speed of this journey? [2]

_____

_____ m/s

(c) Calculate the speed for the first part of the journey. [2]

_____ m/s

(d) On a distance–time graph, what would a curved line indicate? [1]

_____

18. **(a)** Complete the following sentences. Use words from this list. [3]

constant   changing   speeding up   slowing down   stationary

On a distance–time graph, if the motion of an object is represented by a curved line, then the

speed of the object is _____. If the gradient is increasing, the object

is _____. If the gradient is decreasing, then the object is

_____.

(b) The graph shows a runner's journey. What is the average speed of this journey? [2]

_____

_____

_____ m/s

19. Alex is practising driving his car. The velocity–time graph shows his journey. Describe the motion of the car during each stage of the journey.

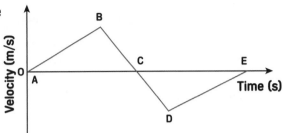

🖉 *The quality of written communication will be assessed in your answer to this question.* [6]

_____

_____

_____

_____

_____

20. Tina was riding her bike to the shops from her house. She travelled at 5m/s for 20 seconds, then gradually slowed down over 10 seconds to come to rest at the shop 130m from the start position.

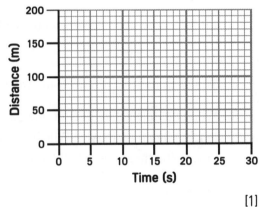

(a) Draw a distance–time graph of Tina's journey on the grid provided. [2]

(b) On her way back from the shops, Tina stops to talk to a friend 20m away from the shops. What is Tina's displacement from her house? [1]

_____ m

(c) Tina and her bike have a combined mass of 70kg. At one point in her journey she and her bike have kinetic energy of 560J. The formula for calculating kinetic energy is:

Kinetic energy = $\frac{1}{2}$ × Mass × Velocity^2

Use the formula to calculate Tina's velocity. Include units in your answer. [3]

_____

_____

_____

[Total: .... / 24]

1. Complete the following sentences. Use words from this list. You may use them more than once. [5]

current   linear   related   unchanged

voltage   correlation   halved

resistance   proportional   doubled

The graph shows how the .... through a resistor changes

as the .... across the resistor changes. The straight line

tells you that the current is .... to the

.... across the resistor. So if the value of the voltage

is doubled, the current flowing is ....

2. This question is about static electricity.

(a) When a plastic rod is rubbed with a cloth, the rod becomes positively charged. Which of the statements below is correct? Put a tick (✓) in the box next to the correct statement. [1]

The rod is positively charged because it has gained electrons. ☐

Protons have been rubbed off the cloth onto the rod. ☐

The rod has lost electrons. ☐

The cloth has lost electrons to the rod. ☐

(b) When aeroplanes fly through the air, they can become charged. They need to be discharged on landing by an earth wire. Which of the statements below are correct? Put ticks (✓) in the boxes next to the **three** correct statements. [3]

The earth wire is an insulator. ☐

Positive ions will move up the wire to cancel out the electrons. ☐

There are free electrons in the wire to allow a current to flow. ☐

A current will flow in the wire. ☐

The resistance of the wire is large. ☐

Some energy in the wire will be lost as heat on discharge. ☐

(c) A person rubs a Perspex rod with a cloth and the Perspex rod becomes negatively charged. The rod is then suspended from a clamp stand using insulated string. Another Perspex rod, which has also been rubbed with the same type of cloth, is brought near to it. Describe what will happen. [1]

....

3. This question is about components in a series circuit. The diagram shows a series circuit containing two resistors, R_1 and R_2, powered by a battery.

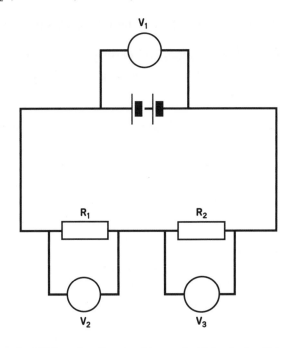

(a) (i) If voltmeter V_1 reads 20V and voltmeter V_3 reads 8V, what will be the reading on voltmeter V_2? [2]

....

.... volts

(ii) If a current of 2A flows in the circuit and voltmeter V_3 reads 8V, what will be the value of the resistance R_1? [2]

....

.... Ω

(b) Resistor R_1 is replaced in the circuit by a resistor of 16Ω. Voltmeter V_3 now reads 4V. The reading on voltmeter V_1 remains 20V.

(i) What current would now flow in the circuit? [2]

....

.... amps

(ii) How much work is done when 3 units of charge (coulombs) flow through the 16Ω resistor? [2]

....

.... joules

(c) Resistor R_2 is replaced by a thermistor. The current flowing is measured as 0.5A. The resistance of R_1 is 16Ω. V_1 still reads 20V.

Explain what would happen in the circuit if the thermistor was placed into a beaker of ice.

You will need to consider what will happen to the resistance of the thermistor and how that would alter the current flowing in the circuit. You should also consider what changes might occur to the readings shown on the voltmeters.

✎ *The quality of written communication will be assessed in your answer to this question.* [6]

....

....

....

....

....

....

4. Complete the following sentences. Use words from this list. [4]

volts	charge	used	amps	conductors
not used	positive ions	insulators	protons	

An electric current is a flow of .... It is measured in ....

Metals are .... as there are lots of charges free to move. A battery can make

these charges move and they are .... up as they flow around a circuit.

5. Wasim sets up the circuit shown in the diagram. When he closes the switch, the resistor gets hot. Explain why that happens. [4]

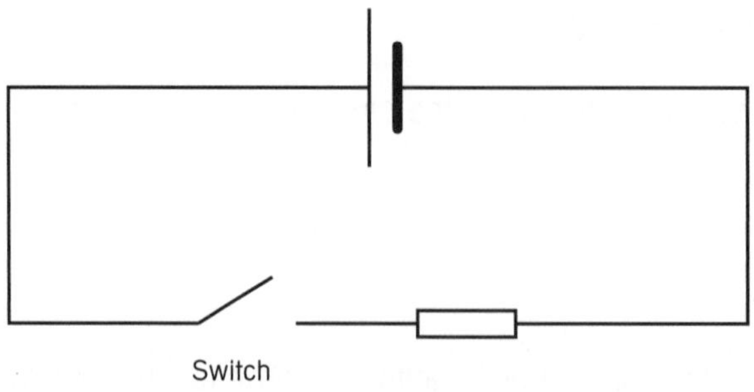

Switch

....

....

....

6. A group of students is discussing moving magnets in coils of wire.

Chevelle
When I move a magnet towards a coil of wire, a voltage is induced across the coil.

Toni
The faster I move the magnet towards the coil, the larger the induced voltage.

Jason
If I wrap the coil of wire around a piece of copper, then move the magnet towards the coil, I will get a bigger voltage than before.

Yvonne
If I reverse the magnet, the induced voltage will also be reversed when I move the magnet towards the coil.

(a) Which student is making an incorrect statement? [1]

_____

(b) Which student is talking about the rate at which field lines are cut? [1]

_____

7. This question is about the motor effect.

The diagram shows a wire carrying a current placed in a magnetic field.

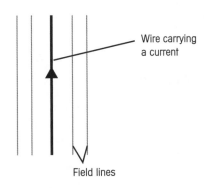

Wire carrying a current

Field lines

P5 Electric Circuits

(a) Which of the statements below is correct? Put a tick (✓) in the box next to the correct statement. [1]

Increasing the current will increase the force on the wire. ☐

Reversing the current will produce a force in the opposite direction. ☐

Increasing the strength of the magnetic field will increase the size of the force on the wire. ☐

There will be no force on the wire. ☐

(b) When a magnet is moved into a coil of wire connected to an ammeter, it indicates that a current is flowing. Describe **two** ways to produce a current in the opposite direction. [2]

1. ....

2. ....

(c) Electricity can be produced by rotating a magnet inside a coil of wire. An induced voltage will be produced across the coil. Below are some statements about possible changes that can be made.

A Using a larger number of turns on the coil

B Turning the magnet slowly and steadily

C Using a stronger magnet

D Turning the magnet around before allowing it to rotate

Which combination of changes will result in an **increased** induced voltage? Put a tick (✓) in the box next to the correct answer. [1]

A and C ☐

A and D ☐

B and C ☐

Another combination ☐

8. This question is about using the mains supply to power electrical devices.

(a) A 1.84kW electric fire runs off the 230V mains.

(i) What current does it take? [2]

....

.... A

(ii) What is the resistance of the fire? [2]

....

.... Ω

(b) Three bulbs, each with a resistance of 460Ω, are connected in parallel across the 230V mains.

(i) What is the current that the mains must provide in order to light all the lamps normally? [2]

....

....

....

.... A

(ii) If the bulbs are now arranged in series and light up, they will be dimmer. What current will flow through them? [2]

....

.... A

9. Lam is a student. He wants to demonstrate how the resistance of an LDR (light dependent resistor) depends on the brightness of a lamp. He has been given a battery, an LDR, some connecting leads, an ammeter and a working high-powered torch.

Describe an experiment that Lam could do to show how the resistance of an LDR varies with the brightness of the light. You could start by drawing a circuit diagram and explaining what readings need to be taken and how they are going to be recorded.

✎ The quality of written communication will be assessed in your answer to this question. [6]

....

....

....

....

....

....

10. Chloe has been given a component which has been placed in a box with a connecting wire attached to each end and a small hole in the box just above the component. The component, which also had a voltmeter connected in parallel with it, was then placed in a series circuit with a battery and an ammeter. By moving a torch close to the hole in the box above the component, she recorded the following readings:

Distance of the Torch from Component (cm)	Voltage (V)	Current (A)	Resistance (Ω)
20	6	0.6	10
40	6	0.5	12
60	6		15
80	6	0.3	
100	6	0.2	30

(a) (i) Complete the table by filling in the missing values for current and resistance. [2]

(ii) What component was most likely to be in the box? [1]

(b) Chloe thinks that there is a negative correlation between the current and the distance the torch is from the component. Do her results support this conclusion? Explain your answer. [2]

(c) Chloe wants to have more confidence in her conclusion and asks four friends how to improve the experiment.

Charlie
Repeat the readings lots of times.

Jo-Shun
Repeat the experiment using a higher voltage.

Toni
Repeat the experiment using a larger range of distances.

Faye
Draw a graph to see if there are any outliers.

Who gives the best advice? Explain your answer. [2]

11. The diagram shows a series circuit where a battery lights two identical bulbs. Also connected in the circuit are three ammeters, A_1, A_2 and A_3, and three voltmeters, V_1, V_2 and V_3. The values of one ammeter and one voltmeter are shown. What are the values of the others? [4]

A_1: .... A

A_3: .... A

V_2: V

V_3: V

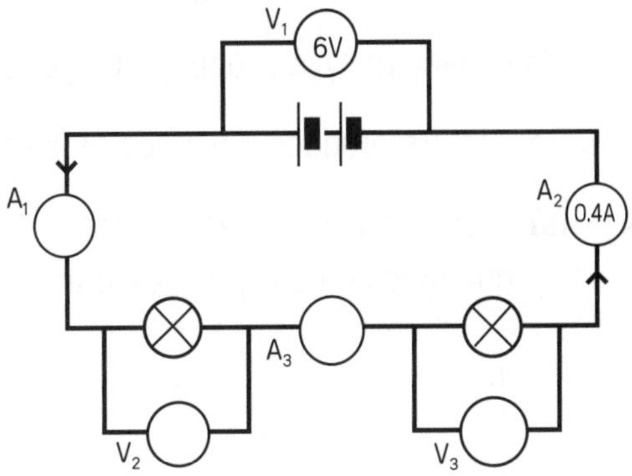

12. This question is about components in an electrical circuit.

(a) (i) Describe what happens to a component when a current passes through it. [1]

....

(ii) All components in a circuit have resistance. Why can the resistance of wires be ignored when doing calculations on small circuits? [1]

....

....

....

(b) Some students made the following statements. Which of them are true? Put ticks (✓) in the boxes next to the **two** correct statements. [2]

The greater the voltage across a component, the greater the current flowing through it. ☐

A component with 6V across it and having a resistance of 4Ω will have a current of 2A through it. ☐

In an insulator, there are lots of charges free to move. ☐

Two insulators with similar charges will repel each other. ☐

(c) Describe the difference between a direct current (d.c.) from a battery and an alternating current (a.c.) from the mains. [1]

....

....

....

P5 | Electric Circuits

13. Which of the following statements is **not** true? Put a tick (✓) in the box next to the **incorrect** statement.   [1]

The voltage of the mains supply is 230V.

A transformer can change the size of a direct current (d.c.).

Mains electricity is produced by generators.

Generators produce a voltage by electromagnetic induction.

14. **(a)** You have been given an electric motor which is running as it is connected to a battery. What **three** changes could you make to the system in order to make your motor run faster?   [3]

1. ....

2. ....

3. ....

(b) Explain why an electric motor has a commutator.   [2]

....

....

....

15. The symbols below are for components that are found in an electric circuit. Draw straight lines from the symbols to the correct names.   [3]

Symbol   **Name**

Battery

Thermistor

Variable resistor

LDR

[Total: .... / 77]

16. This question is about an a.c. generator.

(a) Why is a voltage induced across a coil of wire by the rotation of a magnet near to it? [1]

....

....

....

(b) Describe how the size of the induced voltage across the coil of the generator changes and how its direction changes during each rotation of the magnet.

✎ *The quality of written communication will be assessed in your answer to this question.* [6]

....

....

....

....

....

....

17. A thermistor is connected in series with a red lamp to form one branch of a circuit. An LDR is connected in series with a blue lamp to form another branch of the circuit. Both branches are now connected in parallel across a battery.

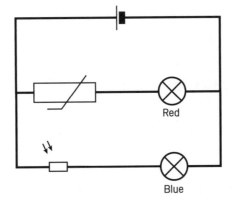

Below are some statements.

A If the room heats up, the blue lamp will come on.

B To get the red lamp on, I have to switch off the light in the room.

C If it is hot in the room and I increase the brightness of the room, both the red and the blue lights come on.

D If the room gets colder and brighter, only the blue light comes on.

E If the blue light is on and I put the thermistor in ice, the blue light goes off.

Which of the statements are true? Put a tick (✓) in the box next to the combination of statements that is correct. [1]

A and D ☐   C, D and E ☐

B and D ☐   C and D ☐

A, B and E ☐

18. Which of the following statements is **not** true about a series circuit? Put a tick (✓) in the box next to the **incorrect** statement. [1]

The potential difference is largest across a large resistor, because more work is done by the charge moving through a large resistor than through a small one. ☐

A change in the resistance of one component in the circuit will not affect the potential differences across the other components. ☐

If a thermistor is connected in series with two fixed resistors, the potential difference across the fixed resistors will increase if the thermistor gets hot. ☐

The work done on each unit charge by the battery must equal the work done by it on the circuit components. ☐

19. This question is about how much energy appliances use.

Priscilla had a heater on for 2 days and it costs her 768p at a rate of 8p per kWh.

(a) How much energy did the heater use? [2]

....

.... kWh

(b) What power rating was the heater? [2]

....

.... kW

(c) She changed the heater and replaced it with a 250W heater. The cost of using this heater was 40p at the same rate of 8p per kWh. How long was the heater on for? [2]

....

....

.... hours

20. Below are some statements about how a transformer works. They are not in the correct order. Put the statements in the correct order by writing the letters in the empty boxes. [4]

A The alternating magnetic field keeps changing direction in the iron core inside the secondary coil.

B The alternating magnetic field changes direction in the iron core with the same frequency as the applied alternating voltage.

C The alternating current in the primary coil produces an alternating magnetic field.

D An alternating potential difference is induced in the secondary coil.

E An alternating voltage is applied to the primary coil.

Start					

21. This question is about transformers.

(a) Explain how a step-down transformer, as used in a mobile phone charger, changes the 230V mains supply to 2.3V.

In your answer, you will need to consider how a voltage is induced in the secondary coil.

🖉 *The quality of written communication will be assessed in your answer to this question.* [6]

_____

_____

_____

_____

_____

_____

_____

(b) A transformer has 40 turns on the primary coil and 320 turns on the secondary coil. If the output voltage is 160V, what is the voltage across the primary coil? [2]

_____

_____

_____ V

[Total: _____ / 27]

1. Rutherford, Geiger and Marsden carried out an alpha scattering experiment using gold. Below are some possible conclusions resulting from this experiment.

A The nucleus is very dense.

B An atom is mainly empty space.

C The nucleus is surrounded by negative electrons.

D The nucleus has a positive charge.

E Alpha particles must be negatively charged.

F The nucleus is very dense because it is not removed by alpha particles.

Which of the statements were **not** conclusions resulting from this experiment? Put a tick (✓) in the box next to the correct combination of statements. [1]

A and D ☐   A and F ☐   D and F ☐   C and E ☐   B and D ☐

2. Draw a straight line from each type of ionising radiation to the correct statement about its penetrating power. [2]

Radiation	Penetrating power
Alpha	Stopped by 4mm of aluminium but not by paper
Beta	Only stopped by several centimetres of lead
Gamma	Stopped by paper

3. Which one of the following items could not give off radiation that contributes to the background count measured by a Geiger counter? Put a tick (✓) in the box next to the correct answer. [1]

A piece of granite rock ☐   A microwave oven ☐

A piece of concrete ☐   A container of radon gas ☐

4. A report has been produced looking at the risk to health of radon gas. Exposure to radon is thought to increase the risk of developing lung cancer. Data from 13 studies carried out by scientists in nine European countries was used to produce the report. 7000 individual cases of lung cancer were studied and they showed a strong link between exposure to radon gas in the home and lung cancer.

(a) (i) Why would scientists have confidence in the report? [1]

....

(ii) Why would scientists look at the link between radon gas and lung cancer rather than other forms of cancer? [2]

....

....

....

(b) Explain why some scientists might question the correlation mentioned in the report.　　[6]

🖉 *The quality of written communication will be assessed in your answer to this question.*

....

....

....

....

....

....

....

....

....

....

5. Below are some statements about atoms. Put a tick (✓) in the box next to the correct statement.　　[1]

An atom consists of a nucleus containing protons with neutrons in orbit around it. ☐

The nucleus of an atom contains protons and electrons. ☐

Neutrons are positively charged particles in the nucleus. ☐

There are only protons and neutrons in the nucleus of an atom. ☐

The nucleus of an atom is always radioactive. ☐

6. This question is about ionising radiation and its possible effects on the body.

(a) Complete the following sentences. Use words from this list. You may use the words more than once.

Alpha　　Beta　　Gamma

(i) .... radiation causes harm if absorbed by cells but usually passes

through the body without serious damage.　　[1]

(ii) .... radiation is the most dangerous when the source is outside the

body because it can penetrate the skin, causing internal damage.　　[1]

(iii) .... radiation is the most dangerous if the source is inside the body

as it is absorbed by cells in the body.　　[1]

(iv) .... radiation is used to sterilise surgical instruments after they have

been washed.　　[1]

(b) A teacher wants to demonstrate that certain materials can stop ionising radiation. He has three radioactive sources, each giving off a different ionising radiation. He also has a Geiger counter, a stopwatch, a piece of paper, a 4mm thick sheet of aluminium and a thick piece of lead.

(i) Explain how he could use the equipment safely to demonstrate the penetration properties of each ionising radiation.

✎ The quality of written communication will be assessed in your answer to this question. [6]

_____

_____

_____

_____

_____

_____

_____

(ii) Which ionising radiation has the greatest penetration? [1]

_____

(iii) What other reading might the teacher take, using the stopwatch and Geiger counter, to make sure his results were accurate? [1]

_____

_____

(c) (i) Why would a teacher be worried about being exposed to ionising radiation from a source in a laboratory but would not be worried about being exposed to background radiation? [2]

_____

_____

_____

(ii) What is the unit used to measure a dose of radiation? [1]

_____

(iii) What does the word **irradiation** mean? [1]

_____

7. This question is about the uses of radiation.

(a) A patient is to have radioactive iodine injected into his body to treat a thyroid tumour. This will involve a doctor deciding what radioactive source to use, a radiologist preparing the radioactive iodine, a porter to take the patient to and from the radiology area in the hospital and a nurse to look after the patient whilst the activity of the radiation in the patient's body decreases to a safe level after a few days.

(i) Which person will receive the highest lifetime dose of radiation? [1]

....

(ii) Which person suffers contamination? [1]

....

(iii) All five people will have been exposed to radiation. What word is used to describe this exposure to radiation? [1]

....

(b) Another patient is in the hospital awaiting treatment for thyroid cancer. He is given a leaflet containing some information on the procedure. It says that radioiodine will be used, which emits beta particles and has a half-life of eight days.

The patient is also given advice on what to do after the treatment:

- You must remain in hospital for a few days.

- You must be in a single room.

- You must not get close to any visitors in hospital.

The nurse advises the patient not to hug any relatives who come in to see him in the next few days. Why is that? [2]

....

....

....

8. This question is about whether a drug should be made available to treat a type of cancer. Read the article.

> Scientists carrying out research into a previously untreatable form of cancer have found some positive results from their tests.
>
> By adding a radioactive isotope to a certain antibody, scientists can target the tumours.
>
> Tumours are exposed to radiation for a few days but there is little damage to healthy cells. From a sample of 15 patients, 10 showed signs of responding either partially or fully to the drug.

(a) What type of radiation is likely to be emitted from the radioactive source? [1]

....

(b) Explain, giving your reasons, which source would be the most suitable to provide the radioactive isotope: a source with a half-life of a few hours, one with a half-life of a few days or one with a half-life of a few weeks.

✎ *The quality of written communication will be assessed in your answer to this question.*   [6]

....

....

....

....

....

....

9.   This question is about radioactive sources and their properties.

The table gives information about four radioactive sources.

Source	Half-life	Radiation Emitted
W	1 hour	Alpha
X	40 years	Beta
Y	300 years	Alpha
Z	4 hours	Gamma

(a) Using the information in the table, choose the best source to match each of these uses.

(i) A source for a smoke detector which must have a short range and a small power of penetration.   [1]

....

(ii) A source to act as a tracer with strong penetrating powers.   [1]

....

(iii) A source to measure the thickness of thin aluminium cans on a conveyor belt.   [1]

....

(b) Below are some statements about radioactive elements. Put ticks (✓) in the boxes next to the **three** correct statements. [3]

The time taken for a radioactive source to become safe is called the half-life. ☐

The half-life is a measurement of the background radiation. ☐

The activity of a radioactive source is constant. ☐

The time taken for the activity of a radioactive source to fall to half of its starting value is called the half-life. ☐

The term half-life can only be used with sources that emit gamma radiation. ☐

Most radioactive sources have the same half-life. ☐

The further you are from a radioactive source, the less radiation your body is exposed to. ☐

If you heat a radioactive source strongly, it will give off less radiation. ☐

Lead shields are used in hospitals to protect medical staff from exposure to radiation. ☐

Sources used inside the body have a long half-life. ☐

10. Complete the following sentences. Use words from this list. [3]

half-life   **background count**   **alpha**   **beta**   **gamma**

Chloe measured the time that the activity of a radioactive source took to fall from 60 decays per

minute to 30 decays per minute. This time is called the _____ .

She found that the source emitted _____ radiation as the radiation was stopped by

paper. She said that if she had used _____ radiation, she would have needed

aluminium to stop it.

11. This question is about people who work with radioactive sources.

(a) (i) Why must exposure times be monitored for people who work with radioactive materials? [1]

_____

_____

(ii) Name one job in which a person is likely to come into contact with radiation. [1]

_____

(b) (i) Exposure to ionising radiation is known to be a cause of body cells developing cancer. Explain how ionising radiation can be used to treat and kill cancer cells. [2]

(ii) When treating cancer patients with ionising radiation, what are the dangers to the following people? [2]

The patient: ....

The medical staff: ....

(c) Give **two** precautions a person should take when working with radioactive sources. [2]

1. ....

2. ....

12. Below are some statements about radiation.

A Ionising radiation can be used as a tracer inside the body.

B Most radioactive waste from a power station is high-level waste.

C All elements emit ionising radiation.

D Low-level radioactive waste can be sealed and placed in landfill sites.

E Background radiation is the same throughout the UK.

Which of the statements are correct? Put a tick (✓) in the box next to the correct combination of statements. [1]

A and B ☐   A and D ☐   B, C and D ☐   A, C and E ☐

A, B and D ☐   B and E ☐   A, B and E ☐

13. Name **four** causes of background radiation. [4]

1. ....   2. ....

3. ....   4. ....

[Total: .... / 64]

Higher Tier

14. Below are nuclear equations for the decay of a uranium atom by emission of an alpha particle and for thorium as it decays by emitting a beta particle.

$$U_{92}^{238} \longrightarrow Th_{90}^{v} + He_{w}^{4}$$

$$Th_{90}^{x} \longrightarrow Pa_{91}^{234} + e_{y}^{0}$$

Four numbers have been replaced by letters. What numbers do v, w, x and y represent?   [4]

v: .... w: ....

x: .... y: ....

15. This question is about radioactive decay.

(a) A group of students carried out an experiment to measure the half-life of protactinium using a stopwatch and a Geiger counter. Their results are shown in the table.

Time Measured (minutes)	0	1	2	3	4	5
Activity (counts per second)	251	127	63	31	30	7

(i) From the table, what is the best value for the half-life? Put a tick (✓) in the box next to the best answer.   [1]

1 minute   ☐

30 seconds   ☐

2 minutes   ☐

There is not enough information to calculate it.   ☐

(ii) The students made a mistake recording their data. At what time did they record their outlier? Put a ring around the correct answer.   [1]

1 minute   **2 minutes**   **3 minutes**   **4 minutes**   **5 minutes**

(b) One of the students weighed out 208g of a radioactive isotope which has a half-life of 3 days. How much of the isotope would be left after 15 days?   [2]

....

.... g

(c) A radioactive isotope decays by emitting two alpha particles. Describe the changes in the nucleus of this isotope after emitting the two alpha particles. [2]

16. In a nuclear reactor, uranium is used to produce heat energy in the production of electricity. This question is about how the uranium fuel rods get hot and how the nuclear reactor is controlled.

(a) What happens when uranium undergoes nuclear fission?

✎ *The quality of written communication will be assessed in your answer to this question.* [6]

(b) Nuclear fission can lead to a chain reaction. Briefly describe what happens in a chain reaction. [2]

(c) Explain how the chain reaction is controlled. [2]

17. Below are some statements about the differences between nuclei of the same element. Put ticks (✓) in the boxes next to the **two** correct statements. [2]

Isotopes of the same element always have the same number of protons. ☐

The number of neutrons in isotopes of the same element is always the same. ☐

All isotopes of an element are radioactive. ☐

Isotopes of an element always have the same half-life. ☐

Isotopes of an element always have the same number of protons but a different number of neutrons. ☐

Isotopes of an element always have the same number of neutrons but a different number of protons. ☐

18. This question is about radioactive decay.

(a) Explain one way in which ionising radiation emitted during the radioactive decay of a nucleus can be used as a tracer in the body. What safety procedures need to be considered? [4]

....

....

....

....

....

....

(b) If thorium (atomic number 90) was to emit one alpha particle and two beta particles, what nuclei would be produced? Put a tick (✓) in the box next to the correct answer. [1]

An isotope of thorium, atomic number 90 ☐

An isotope of uranium, atomic number 92 ☐

An isotope of protactinium, atomic number 91 ☐

19. This question is about the nucleus and the energy that can be liberated from it.

(a) The nucleus of an atom consists of protons and neutrons packed together. The protons carry a positive charge and neutrons have no charge. Explain why the nucleus does not disintegrate. [2]

(b) When a nucleus of uranium-235 fissions into barium-141 and krypton-92, the change in mass is 3.1×10^{-28}kg.

(i) Calculate the energy released by the fission of one uranium nucleus. [2]

.... J

(ii) Calculate how many nuclei must undergo fission in order to release 1.0J of energy by this reaction. [2]

[Total: .... / 33]

Periodic Table

Key

relative atomic mass
atomic symbol
name
atomic (proton) number

1	2											3	4	5	6	7	0
																	4 **He** helium 2
7 **Li** lithium 3	9 **Be** beryllium 4											11 **B** boron 5	12 **C** carbon 6	14 **N** nitrogen 7	16 **O** oxygen 8	19 **F** fluorine 9	20 **Ne** neon 10
23 **Na** sodium 11	24 **Mg** magnesium 12											27 **Al** aluminium 13	28 **Si** silicon 14	31 **P** phosphorus 15	32 **S** sulfur 16	35.5 **Cl** chlorine 17	40 **Ar** argon 18
39 **K** potassium 19	40 **Ca** calcium 20	45 **Sc** scandium 21	48 **Ti** titanium 22	51 **V** vanadium 23	52 **Cr** chromium 24	55 **Mn** manganese 25	56 **Fe** iron 26	59 **Co** cobalt 27	59 **Ni** nickel 28	63.5 **Cu** copper 29	65 **Zn** zinc 30	70 **Ga** gallium 31	73 **Ge** germanium 32	75 **As** arsenic 33	79 **Se** selenium 34	80 **Br** bromine 35	84 **Kr** krypton 36
85 **Rb** rubidium 37	88 **Sr** strontium 38	89 **Y** yttrium 39	91 **Zr** zirconium 40	93 **Nb** niobium 41	96 **Mo** molybdenum 42	[98] **Tc** technetium 43	101 **Ru** ruthenium 44	103 **Rh** rhodium 45	106 **Pd** palladium 46	108 **Ag** silver 47	112 **Cd** cadmium 48	115 **In** indium 49	119 **Sn** tin 50	122 **Sb** antimony 51	128 **Te** tellurium 52	127 **I** iodine 53	131 **Xe** xenon 54
133 **Cs** caesium 55	137 **Ba** barium 56	139 **La*** lanthanum 57	178 **Hf** hafnium 72	181 **Ta** tantalum 73	184 **W** tungsten 74	186 **Re** rhenium 75	190 **Os** osmium 76	192 **Ir** iridium 77	195 **Pt** platinum 78	197 **Au** gold 79	201 **Hg** mercury 80	204 **Tl** thallium 81	207 **Pb** lead 82	209 **Bi** bismuth 83	[209] **Po** polonium 84	[210] **At** astatine 85	[222] **Rn** radon 86
[223] **Fr** francium 87	[226] **Ra** radium 88	[227] **Ac*** actinium 89	[261] **Rf** rutherfordium 104	[262] **Db** dubnium 105	[266] **Sg** seaborgium 106	[264] **Bh** bohrium 107	[277] **Hs** hassium 108	[268] **Mt** meitnerium 109	[271] **Ds** darmstadtium 110	[272] **Rg** roentgenium 111							

1 **H** hydrogen 1

Elements with atomic numbers 112–116 have been reported but not fully authenticated.

*The lanthanoids (atomic numbers 58–71) and the actinoids (atomic numbers 90–103) have been omitted.
The relative atomic masses of copper and chlorine have not been rounded to the nearest whole number.

Data Sheet

Qualitative Analysis

Tests for Positively Charged Ions

Ion	Test	Observation
Calcium Ca^{2+}	Add dilute sodium hydroxide	A white precipitate forms; the precipitate does not dissolve in excess sodium hydroxide
Copper Cu^{2+}	Add dilute sodium hydroxide	A light blue precipitate forms; the precipitate does not dissolve in excess sodium hydroxide
Iron(II) Fe^{2+}	Add dilute sodium hydroxide	A green precipitate forms; the precipitate does not dissolve in excess sodium hydroxide
Iron(III) Fe^{3+}	Add dilute sodium hydroxide	A red-brown precipitate forms; the precipitate does not dissolve in excess sodium hydroxide
Zinc Zn^{2+}	Add dilute sodium hydroxide	A white precipitate forms; the precipitate dissolves in excess sodium hydroxide

Tests for Negatively Charged Ions

Ion	Test	Observation
Carbonate CO_3^{2-}	Add dilute acid	The solution effervesces; carbon dioxide gas is produced (the gas turns limewater from colourless to milky)
Chloride Cl^-	Add dilute nitric acid, then add silver nitrate	A white precipitate forms
Bromide Br^-	Add dilute nitric acid, then add silver nitrate	A cream precipitate forms
Iodide I^-	Add dilute nitric acid, then add silver nitrate	A yellow precipitate forms
Sulfate SO_4^{2-}	Add dilute nitric acid, then add barium chloride or barium nitrate	A white precipitate forms

Data Sheet

Useful Relationships

Explaining Motion

$$\text{Speed} = \frac{\text{Distance travelled}}{\text{Time taken}}$$

$$\text{Acceleration} = \frac{\text{Change in velocity}}{\text{Time taken}}$$

Momentum = Mass × Velocity

Change of momentum = Resultant force × Time for which it acts

Work done by a force = Force × Distance moved in the direction of the force

Amount of energy transferred = Work done

Change in gravitational potential energy = Weight × Vertical height difference

$$\text{Kinetic energy} = \frac{1}{2} \times \text{Mass} \times [\text{Velocity}]^2$$

Electric Circuits

Power = Voltage × Current

$$\text{Resistance} = \frac{\text{Voltage}}{\text{Current}}$$

$$\frac{\text{Voltage across primary coil}}{\text{Voltage across secondary coil}} = \frac{\text{Number of turns in primary coil}}{\text{Number of turns in secondary coil}}$$

Radioactive Materials

Energy = Mass × [Speed of light in a vacuum]^2

Notes